THE NATURAL HEALTH MATRIX

Eastern Wisdom for Western Minds

A Journey to Wellbeing

To Liz & Simon

Thank you both so much for your valuable support and trust, believe in us . . .

With best wishes

Thomas & Vijay

Thomas Mueller

B.A, D.A.Med

THE NATURAL HEALTH MATRIX

Ayuwave Natural Health Clinic
57, Wimpole Street
London, W1G 8YW
United Kingdom
www.ayuwave.com
info@ayuwave.com

Published by KatGab Publishers - www.katgabpublishers.com

Publishing Support and Design: PJ Bradbury, The Writer Way

Graphic Design by Sandra Pieroni

Cover Design: Sandra Pieroni, PJ Bradbury

Elemental Artwork by Justina May Groeber

Proofreading: Wendy & Words, Lisa Honey and Sue Clark

Final typesetting Lisa Honey

"Hold this book in your hands and feel the cosmic vibration of awareness pouring out an ever-present wisdom of the ancient Ayurveda sages. In *The Natural Health Matrix*, Thomas has successfully crossed the time/space/culture/age barrier by designing a global model that addresses the necessity for sustainable wellness that is accessible to each and every person anywhere in the world. I have had the privilege of knowing Thomas both professionally and personally. He is a gentle healer with an awakened heart."

Maya Tiwari, Author, World Spiritual Teacher & CEO of Wise Earth School of Ayurveda, USA. http://wiseearth.com

"Recent years have seen an exponential growth in interest in non-western health care practice and knowledge across the world. *The Natural Health Matrix* provides an excellent resource with which patients and those seeking well-being can explore the relevance and contemporary application of traditional philosophy and teachings to their own health journey. Drawing upon his personal experience and insights, Thomas Mueller has contributed a captivating interpretation of the potential of these traditional systems of thought for modern healing in a way that complements the critical and scientific examination of this significant area of health care."

Professor Jon Adams

Professor of Public Health, Faculty of Health, University of Technology Sydney.

Director, Australian Research Centre in Complementary and Integrative Medicine (ARCCIM)

Dedicated to all those who have
inspired me by showing me that better
health and happiness is always possible
when staying connected to one's
beautiful higher self.

Contents

PREFACE

One, two, three, four, five... Is it possible? An obese couple with their three children on a small scooter, smoky buses with people clinging onto each other like grapes on a grapevine. Cows patiently eating the leftover greens from the morning market. Cyclists and pedestrians everywhere, even a goat. Thick, clawing dust that you can see and taste. Blaring horns and an ocean of black and yellow auto rickshaws push their way through the streets like aggressive wasps fighting over a bit of rotten apple.

"You scared me to death!" I screamed when a long, bony arm finds its way through the partially open window of a Skoda, reaching out for rupees. "Why does everyone keep staring at me? Oh yes, of course..."

I can't believe what I've just gotten myself into...

Perhaps you're one of those people who think first and then, after carefully considering all the pros and cons, take action. And after you have achieved the desired outcome, you allow yourself a feeling of satisfaction. Well, I am certainly not that type. If something feels right, I just go ahead and do it and think later. I don't mean impulsive action. It is something that resonates from deep within, perhaps what could be called intuitive knowledge. So if you are curious as to why a westerner like me got into Ayurveda, this is exactly the reason; nothing more, nothing less. It just felt right at the time.

Making My Own Life Change

This goes back to the spring of 1988 when I learned how to meditate. I hadn't even turned twenty yet and was working as a government official in Germany. Today I would describe that lifestyle as inactive and boring. The only thing that brought some kind of excitement into my life was playing the drums in a brass band and my involvement with a local amateur theatre group. On one hand, I loved performing in front of an audience but, on the other hand, I suffered from terrible stage fright to the extent that I developed a pattern of bad stomach cramps, followed by frequent visits to the bathroom about three hours prior to any performance. Today this would perhaps be diagnosed as anxiety nervosa, diarrhoea being one of its accompanying symptoms. This led me to join a meditation course to learn how to handle anxiety and stressful events and to gain confidence in myself.

As the youngest and the heaviest of five boys, I grew up in a conservative rural village with 2,000 people in south-west Germany, close to the French border. This was twenty-five years ago, at a time and in a place where nobody had even heard of Ayurveda. Trying to pronounce the Sanskrit word properly was a major challenge in itself. Back then I was ignorant about any mind-body approach to health in which the dominating role of the mind and its effect on the body is recognised. The concept of prevention and wellbeing wasn't known. In fact, I tried hard to fit in with friends and colleagues and made myself relax by having a few drinks on a regular basis, especially at the weekend. My self-confidence grew and so did my tummy. My staple diet consisted of sugary pastries, plenty of bread, pasta and potatoes and, of course, a good schnitzel with a thick creamy sauce mixed with fresh vegetables from our own garden.

Then, after practising my newly acquired 'yogic' skill for a couple of weeks or so, something unexpected and extraordinary emerged: the quest to search for a deeper meaning in my life somehow became stronger. I realised that if I continued to live my life the way I was, I might end up becoming an alcoholic with high blood pressure and dying of a stroke or heart attack. When I looked in the mirror I began to notice a rash developing around my mouth and I was disgusted with my body. I began to tolerate less and less alcohol and I found it increasingly difficult to eat the meat my mum prepared.

Biting the Bullet

I visited my doctor, mainly because I struggled walking uphill or when climbing stairs. I developed frequent migraine attacks, my rash got worse and the list of ailments grew. Through a blood test we found out that my liver was in a mess, I had a mercury allergy and animal protein no longer suited me.

A few days passed and, one morning after meditating, I began a conversation with myself in the mirror, realising that I was no longer able to fit into my nice shirts. I have always loved wearing unusual, stylish clothing but it was becoming more difficult to find anything that would fit me. It was then I realised that I could not expect things to change if I kept doing the same things over and over again. So I decided that morning... *Right, this is it. It's time for a change.*

For six weeks I followed a strict dietary regime: no breakfast; one heavy meal at lunch, consisting of a large steak or other lean meat and mountains of salad; fruit and yoghurt later in the afternoon; and nothing after 6 pm. No pastries and no alcohol during that time. After sticking to this high protein diet for six weeks, I went from 88 kilograms down to 68 kilograms. The excitement of having lost all that weight within a relatively short period of time was reason enough for me to ignore my protein allergy and the happily flourishing skin rash.

Looking back, it was the meditation that helped me get in touch with myself and made me want to make the changes that I had to make, without anybody telling me to do so. I managed to lose my mental obesity first, which in turn helped me to lose the physical weight. I am certainly not advocating any particular diet or claiming that meditation is the answer to weight problems; I am just sharing my personal health journey here and reflecting on the role of the mind when addressing any health issue.

I was very naive. I had no idea what I was getting myself into that spring in 1988 but I totally trusted the process and went with the flow. I had my mercury fillings removed, stopped drinking alcohol and became a vegetarian for the next twenty years. As a result, my skin improved, I had fewer migraine attacks and most important of all, I managed to keep the weight off. Overall I was less stressed and felt happier and more confident with myself.

Making the Breakthrough with Ayurveda

Coming back to my original question, "Why Ayurveda?" ... Well, first let me explain what Ayurveda is:

Ayurveda is the knowledge of how to live a long and healthy life and is a system of health care originating from India thousands of years ago. It can be seen as the mother of all natural therapies, which uses the inherent principles of nature to restore health and wellbeing in an individual on the level of body, mind and the non-physical.

Within a few months of learning to meditate, I found myself visiting one of the first Ayurvedic clinics in Germany with a naturopathic friend of mine, in the Black Forest, when I was approached by the medical director who had an application form in his hand. "This is for you," he said. "There is a four-week intensive training course in Ayurveda and I want to see you there." Not really knowing how or why this came about, I did not respond; but somehow, deep within myself, I knew that this was it. I had to make it happen and attend this course. I didn't know at the time that the close naturopathic friend was to become my wife a couple of years later. Today I am extremely grateful to her for setting me up on the path to discovering the 'true me'.

Throughout my personal journey towards self-discovery, personal development and better health, I never questioned anything. I can only say that my life has taken a 360 degree turn and I have never looked back. Here we are in 2014 and it is hard to believe that today I can celebrate my Ayurvedic silver jubilee.

Having experienced the change from the sedentary lifestyle of an administrative government job to thinking as a practitioner, educator, performing artist and a would-be academician, it is with great passion that I share in this book how Ayurveda and its principles have helped me and my clients handle the stress of frequent travels, mental fatigue and physical exhaustion. I share how I overcame food intolerances and how I was able to lose and maintain my weight after having suffered from obesity in my early adulthood.

Perseverance Pays Off

There have been many moments in my life where my only thought was to give up on my Ayurvedic career, thinking it was too difficult to advocate something that is so unknown and non-conventional, especially in the West. Each time I decided to turn my back on Ayurveda, to my surprise it returned like a boomerang, stronger than before. I certainly do not pretend to know all the answers, and upon reflection I now see how life, with all its challenges, has given me the opportunity to grow.

Today I can say I have become slightly more humble and my values have shifted from fanaticism to 'balanced reality', which in itself is the magic potion in Ayurveda. One thing that hasn't changed over the past twenty-five years is the joy and pleasure I derive from eating a piece of cake. The only thing that *has* changed is its recipe.

Ayuwave: A New Holistic Approach to Health through Ayurveda

Over the years, having had the opportunity to teach and practise Ayurveda in many different countries to people of all ages and various cultures, I have finally found my own voice in making Ayurveda relevant to modern-day living. This journey, inspired by immersion in one of the world's most ancient holistic methods of health care gave birth to *Ayuwave*, an approach I employ in my exploration to perfect health. *The Natural Health Matrix* is not an interpretation of a classical Ayurvedic textbook; it is a result of my training in the subtler aspects of Vedic Science, my particular interest in Panchakarma and the growing desire to bring Ayurveda more seriously into clinical practice as an Ayurvedic practitioner. In addition, intensive years of study in Ayurvedic medicine in New Zealand and frequent internships at various Ayurvedic institutions and hospitals around India have allowed me to incorporate the best of East and West in my clinical practice today, all leading to the concepts and approaches of *Ayuwave*.

It is now one of my greatest joys to be able to offer an encapsulation of all the knowledge I have gained in this book *The Natural Health Matrix,* so that I can help even more people to achieve perfect health and wellness. If you are looking for the dos and don'ts of Ayurveda, searching for the perfect diet or a quick fix, or you'd prefer to turn over the responsibility of your health and wellbeing to someone else, then I suggest that you put this book aside and keep searching. There are plenty of other books out there that perhaps will fulfil these needs. But if you're ready to take charge of your health then read on.

There is easy access to a flood of information on how to improve your wellbeing and how to remain healthy and youthful; but deciding what is best for you is a bit like a honeybee attracted by the scent of flowers but unable to choose between the sweetest nectar. *The Natural Health Matrix, Eastern Concepts for Western Minds* can become your Ayurvedic self-help kit. It equips you with practical, easy to incorporate self-help tools that when used properly can become an invaluable instrument to align you with your doctor within. The information in this book will help you to understand your unique Matrix by reconnecting or awakening you to your own inner self-healing ability, the key to repair and rejuvenation. *The Natural Health Matrix* also serves as a guide on how to maintain your newly found health and wellbeing.

It would give me no greater happiness than to know that you have been able to discover that hidden place within you where there is the potential for perfect health and wellbeing – your *Natural Health Matrix* – and then to activate it.

INTRODUCTION

Still, there are times when I wake up sighing before the alarm goes off, only to realise that I have not yet fallen asleep. Times when I struggle and feel like the whole world is against me. In those moments I often find excuses to think that today is not the right moment, only to realise that there is no better moment than this one. It's then, when life forces me to stand still, take account and accept that I have reached a T-junction and must make decisions, that I know I have to change something...

Am I living life or is life living me?

In this book I share with you valuable self-help tools that guide you to unveil your unique *Natural Health Matrix*. The treatment methods, principles and procedures described in this book have been proven highly effective on my own personal Ayurvedic journey to maintaining wellbeing, whilst dealing with the challenges that each day brings. These tools have been developed and tested rigorously over twenty-five years of *Ayuwave* clinical practice and my own personal life experience and with the understanding that each individual is unique. When it comes to health and wellbeing, there is no 'one size fits all' approach.

Why the Matrix?

Let's start to sing from the same song sheet by explaining why I called this book *The Natural Health Matrix*. First of all 'Matrix', in the context of this book, doesn't match any of the explanations that can be found in 'Master Google'.

The term 'Matrix' is used in this book as a metaphor to explain that within each person there is a hidden doorway that provides access to a place where there is the potential for perfect health and wellbeing.

Nature in itself is a perfect example of how to change and adjust to different environments in a silent manner, without much effort. Take the example of how shrubs or the sturdy roots of a tree can break through the toughest concrete. These adjustments and changes happen naturally, without any effort. In essence, you are a reflection of this effortless process of nature and, whilst your body is a fairly permanent and solid structure, it undergoes constant change.

If this is a reality, why can't change be towards the better? The Matrix, as discussed in this book, provides you access to a place where your current state of wellbeing can be transformed into a state that is closer to what can be called 'natural health', where self-repair occurs unforced and where improved wellbeing and youthfulness can become a living reality.

How to Use This Book

Each chapter is related to one of the five elements and begins and ends with a personal story that is connected with the topic discussed in that chapter. You will also find a colour image of the *Ayuwave* elemental art work that has been specifically created to connect to that particular element. Depending on your preferred style of learning and the mood you are in when reading, you can choose to do either one, or all, of the following:

- Read this book from page to page.
- Contemplate on the artwork.
- Get inspired by the stories woven into the text.
- Skip the stories and go straight to the content.
- Reflect on its metaphors.
- Taste the sweet nectar of the book by studying the 'Amrita' section of each chapter, which summarises its essence.
- Take a moment to reflect upon the 'What Ifs' at the end of each chapter.
- Accept the invitation to action.

As you read through the book you will be invited to reflect on your lifestyle and circumstances. If you choose to keep doing what you have been doing, it is impossible to experience change. However, it is my promise to you that if you trust the process, embrace the journey and take action, you will get results. You will be…

- given the tools to unveil your unique Matrix that allows you to get in touch with your doctor within and thereby discover many of the answers to your health challenges
- shown a way to increase the awareness of your own inner healing mechanism and discover that health is a natural state of being, easy to obtain
- able to give up the need to control and, by surrendering to your inner knowledge, able to live life rather than having life live you.

"Rupees, rupees!" cried the man attached to the hand. We are heading towards a T-junction and can only turn right or left.

"Dandu, you are supposed to know the way. I need your help quickly; which way do we go?"

"This way," replied my co-pilot with a big smile on his face, pointing towards the paddy field straight ahead. The noise around me slowly faded and I experienced a total sense of inner calm and peace. The moment I stopped resisting, something else took over and brought us home safely.

There is no better moment than this one. Trust the process and enjoy your journey…

ONE ~ S P A C E

Awareness – The Foundation Of Health And Wellbeing

Over the past months my body had become like a dry sponge, hard and cracking, each cell crying out for that bit of juice to make me come alive again. It was whilst walking barefoot through the luscious, green rainforest in the hinterlands of Melbourne, breathing in the freshest of air, taking a dip in the cleansing waters of a little lake, and bathing in the warm late afternoon sun in such a peaceful and calm atmosphere, only interrupted by the chorus of the most colourful and amazingly beautiful birds, that I realised how much I had missed being able to get in touch with Mother Nature. What an indescribable experience... my favourite bird, the kookaburra, laughed along whilst following me during my exploration through the bushes of the Dandenong National Park.

You may be thinking, 'Are you crazy? How naive is that? Do you not realise that Australia has the most dangerous animals on this planet? Never heard about snakes, spiders, crocodiles and bull ants?'

I went back a couple of years later – the same bush, a similar warm spring day. But this time my mood was dampened by the possible dangers that could await me there. I didn't feel as free as I felt during my first visit. I was walking in my boots on a stable footpath when all of a sudden my heart almost stopped. I could feel the sudden rush of blood to my head, my heart calling 999, making an emergency call to every part of my brain when I saw a black snake curled up on my path, stopping me from continuing my journey though the bush...

In This Chapter We Discuss:

- Awareness and the process of creation.
- Awareness and its role in restoring health and wellbeing.
- The difference between self-awareness and higher awareness.
- The role of the mind in perceiving higher awareness.
- Awareness and its connection to Vedic science.
- Time and awareness.

Why is This Chapter Called 'Space'?

This chapter revolves around the theme of the subtlest and the very first of the five elements – space. The five elements are: space, air, fire, water and earth. All creations, physical and non-physical, occur within space. In other words, creating space is not only the beginning but the only aspect to bring about change. In this context, the change towards creating health and youthfulness also is by understanding the role of the element space. If you are currently experiencing less than perfect health and happiness, and want this to change, you need to create space. The key to creating space is awareness. Changing reality through awareness within all possibilities of the vast space is the beginning of a lifelong journey to health and youthfulness.

Becoming Aware of the Source of Life

Before we explore the concept of awareness any further, I would like you to do the following mental exercise that will provide you the space to listen to what the voice of awareness has to tell you at this particular moment in time.

Call to Action

Close your eyes now and become aware of yourself and your immediate environment. See if you notice any physical sensations as you scan from your head to your toes though your body. Do you experience any colours, sounds or perhaps other sensations such as smells? What about the sounds of your immediate environment? Listen to the chatter in your mind whilst going through this exercise and see if there is any relationship between these sounds and your thoughts. You might perceive an inner voice that questions why you do what you currently do.

Now think: prior to running that scan through your body, you may not have been aware of those pictures, sounds, feelings, thoughts or sensations. You've become more aware through being present, though this awareness has always been there.

Awareness is your innate ability to perceive and, consciously or unconsciously, react to external circumstances. The degree of awareness (and therefore perception) varies and is very much determined by the mind. It is the state of your mind that colours your perception and determines the degree of knowledge. This process gets directed through the senses. Let's take the sense of sight as an example. When your eyes glance across the pages of this book, your mind focuses, through the sense of sight, on the letters of the page in front of you and then interprets these individual letters and gives meaning to the text. So in reading this book with an overcrowded mind, full of thoughts, you understand some of the text that you have just read very differently than you would if reading the same text with a calm and quiet mind. You look through the same eyes, read the same words on the page, but what is different is a mind that is more aware.

Knowledge is different in different states of awareness.

Human awareness can be categorised in two forms:

- self-awareness or awareness of the immediate self, confined by the mind, which makes us read the same lines but interpret them differently, depending on how alert our mind is.
- higher-awareness or awareness of the extended self, which goes beyond the mind. This awareness is pure energy and intelligence. It is there all the time and its essence doesn't change. It permeates anything and everything in creation, from the finest, minute particles of an atom to the gross physical structure of a wooden table. Any experience or object, when broken down to its most basic element, is this heightened awareness. With focused attention in a state of higher awareness you can shift your entire being from the state of ill-health to health. The first step in achieving this goal is to familiarise yourself with the state of self-awareness.

Although self-awareness is restricted and brings about only partial knowledge and understanding, it is the bridge to higher awareness. For many of the clients I see, increasing self-awareness is the first step on their discovery journey of the *Ayuwave* approach to natural health, which will lead them towards improved health and wellbeing. The Matrix is like the door that provides access to heightened awareness, a new world, where healing and repair can be possible.

Self-awareness is very much a reflection of your mind's interpretation of a sensory experience coloured by stored memories. When feeling vulnerable any constructive criticism received can be interpreted as a personal attack. This is an example of how you can become a victim of the senses that coloured your perception of the spoken word; whereas if you receive the same feedback in a state of heightened awareness, you use any suggestion made as constructive critique that may help you to improve and grow.

Energy and intelligence is the connecting fabric that weaves
the entire cosmos into one beautiful piece of tapestry.

Once you have stepped through the invisible veil of the Matrix and have reached a state of heightened awareness, you have access to the knowing that has no boundaries and is the source of all knowledge, of all life, which is the source of infinite energy and intelligence. This source of energy and intelligence is the connecting fabric that weaves the entire cosmos into one beautiful piece of tapestry.

At some time you might have been looking frantically for your glasses in every corner of the house, only to realise after hours of searching that the glasses had actually been sitting on top of your head all that time. Similarly, the key to unlock the *Natural Health Matrix*, which will provide you access to that heightened state of awareness, has always been with you. You have just forgotten it. When you were born, this unlimited awareness of the extended self, the source of energy and intelligence, held your hand and walked with you the first steps of your life. Then, as you grew up, as education, life circumstances and your conditioning shaped your entire being, you let go of that hand and you chose to keep walking your path without this connection.

There was a time during my early adulthood when I was totally unhappy with my circumstances. I was aware of what no longer suited me and that something needed to change, but I had no clue as to what I had to change. It was then, at a point of total frustration, that I naturally seemed to reach out for that hand again, allowing myself to be directed by something bigger than me. Within a short period of time, I was presented with an opportunity to venture into a different career that allowed me to travel the world and teach in many different countries. My life had taken an unexpected turn. What caused the change? Was it sheer luck, my belief in the better or a chance dip into higher awareness that initiated the positive change?

You may have felt similar at times in your life; that something bigger than you provided you protection and/or helped you through difficult phases of your life. This something is the hand of higher-awareness that kept reaching out to you; waiting for the moment you turn around again and grab hold of its hand. Once the connection is re-established, you have opened that door to the source of life, which allows you to create your life the way you envision it to be.

Awareness is the potential for all creation.

Awareness and the Process of Creation

This awareness of the extended self is the skeleton that holds the entire cosmos together. In fact, it can be seen as the source, the course and the goal of all life. Life emerges from pure awareness, awareness stirs the direction of your life and life dissolves again into pure awareness, like the ocean and the wave. The wave gets created at the silent depth of the ocean, when the ocean becomes aware of its immense potential to create innumerable waves in all forms and shapes. This awareness, combined with the intention of the ocean to express itself in the form of a wave, is the starting point of the process of creation. This creates a stir at the bottom of the ocean, which forms the smallest ripple on its surface and finally merges into a huge wave with a distinct shape and form. Then eventually the wave collapses again and becomes one with the ocean.

Awareness is intelligence in motion – the force that creates.

The story of the ocean and the wave remains today more than just a philosophical exploration of the process of creation. Cutting edge discoveries discuss how philosophy and science start to merge. Lynne McTaggert, in her book *The Field,* delves into quantum physics concepts, offering the idea that reality or existence is composed of a concentration of energy that forms objects (including humans) and this energy is also the prime element of awareness. This implies that all matter is connected in waves, tying one part of the universe to every other part. McTaggert also suggests that conscious intentions of humans shape reality through these interactions.

This was confirmed in many ways by Dr Masaru Emoto, in 1999, while conducting research on the formation of water crystals on various stimuli. I won't go into details here because I would not do it justice. However, if you are interested, you can read the book *The Hidden Messages of Water.* As suggested by Masaru, I tried out his theory with a simple experiment using cooked rice poured into two identical jars. On one jar I wrote, "Thank you – I love you" and on the second I wrote, "I hate you –you fool". Both jars were properly sealed, using a lid. For one month, every day I picked up each jar at least once and repeated what was written on the jar. When I spoke to the jar, I really tried to feel the emotions too. After one month, the results were quite mind-blowing. The 'loved' rice was as white and fluffy as the day I put it in there. The 'hated' rice was fermenting and moulding.

This experiment proves how the words you say have a powerful effect on everything around you. Whether it is rice or a human being, your words have a profound impact on others and yourself. Positive words with good intentions behind them nurture and encourage growth. Negative words with negative emotions rot and destroy.

Whatever you put your awareness to grows.

Think about it. Have you ever been around someone who seems to suck the energy out of you? Sometimes this happens even when they don't say anything negative. This is because it is not just what is being said that matters, but it is also what one thinks. Your life is a result of your most common thoughts. If you think great things of yourself, of others and the world around you habitually, then you add to the greatness and nurture the world around. If you complain habitually, criticise and find the bad in others and in most things, then you are responsible, perhaps, for the rice fermenting and moulding. So I encourage you to change your thoughts so they will change your world.

How to Reconnect Again With Higher-Awareness

It is your thoughts that play a major role in allowing you to take control of your life. They grant you access to that heightened awareness that is the potential for all creation. Controlling your thoughts is probably much easier than you think. Just ask yourself 'through which lens am I observing my life currently?' Am I zoomed in and the world I perceive is just grey dust and dirt, or am I viewing my current circumstances through a macroscopic lens where, when zooming out, I recognise that the dust and dirt transform magically into the most beautiful flower? Negative, destructive thoughts and feelings of unhappiness are most likely to be an indication that we view the world through the limitations of the microscopic lens, a restricted mind lacking in awareness. So, the first step to reconnect again with higher awareness is to expand your mind, which controls your thoughts and feelings. In other words, increase self-awareness first.

One of my clients, a thirty-nine-year-old mother with a teenage daughter, visited my practice one day. The primary reason she came was to seek help in coping with an increasingly stressful situation at home. She blamed her daughter and mother-in-law for her misery. I quickly figured out that she had an underlying eating disorder to which she was oblivious. She felt she was eating too much and gaining weight. In fact, just through observation and analysing her daily nutritional routine, she hardly ate at all. She showed clear signs of malnourishment and had a disturbed relationship with food and herself. The first step I took in improving her health was not to focus on how to change her diet or how to manage her stress. It was, instead, to increase self-awareness.

I said, "I would like you to become aware of how your thoughts influence the way you think and feel about yourself. Step out of the picture and look at yourself and your thoughts. No need to analyse, just observe." She came back after three weeks of practising the first step of the *'Ayuwave OBC'* technique (which I will discuss in greater detail in *Chapter Four– The Power of Transformation*) and reported how much this little exercise had helped her to become aware that her self-destructive thoughts and emotions, not the circumstances at home, caused her unhappy relationship with her family.

My experience has often been that as soon as I am aware of what I need to change, I am already half way there. This means being aware that often your thoughts and mental attitude may get in the way of allowing you:

- to experience an improved state of health and wellbeing
- to create the person you want to be
- to live a life you want to live.

It is not the circumstances but our attitudes.

With increased self-awareness you have already climbed half way up a steep and narrow path that leads towards the top of 'the mountain of heightened awareness'. When you have reached its peak, you will see that the world lies at your feet and you will wonder why it has taken you so long to get up there.

The realisation that something needs to change indicates that you are already half way there.

Whilst reading these lines, you might think that the way you live your life currently is perfect and there is nothing you need to change. If that is the case, I congratulate you and perhaps you may choose not to read further. At the same time, I would like to invite you to do a little test with me. Just read through the questions below and if you answer any one of these questions with a 'no', then this is an indicator that your life is not as perfect as it could be.

- Do you feel a sense of ease and lightness in your body?
- Do you feel in charge of your life?
- Do you realise that life does not need to be a struggle?
- Have you found a tool that takes you to the centre of peace within yourself?
- Have you been able to let go of your need to control and, as a result, what you envisioned simply came to you?
- Have you stopped reasoning why things don't work out?
- Can you sense there is something that lies beyond the sky that connects all that is?
- Do you have a sense of trust or inner knowing that all will be fine?
- Are you truly grateful for what you have?

I do not claim that my life is perfect. But I can say that I have learned how to operate what I choose to call *'The Natural Health Matrix'*, which allows me to live life rather than having life living me. There is still a long way to go and plenty of opportunity to explore the functions of its various buttons that help me to restore and maintain my health and wellbeing.

In the following chapters I will go into much greater depth as to how to gain access to this Matrix. But before going there, it is crucial to gain an understanding as to how your mind functions.

The Role of the Mind in Perceiving Higher-Awareness

The mind is the instrument through which you perceive your external world. You might view your external world through the eyes of coloured self-awareness or from the state of uncoloured, extended awareness. Either way, it is your mind which sets the scene. This colour of perception is influenced by present or past experiences. Many factors such as your emotional, physical or mental state of wellbeing, the environment you live in and your culture, education or upbringing alter what you see.

> *"A winner says it's difficult but possible; a loser says it's possible but too difficult."*
>
> Unknown

You can look at any challenging situation in your life from two perspectives. Let's take the following example: as an Ayurvedic practitioner I have received an invitation to present to a group of 50 medical doctors how Ayurveda can be supportive in the treatment of cancer. Either I could say it's difficult but possible or I could have the attitude that it is possible but too difficult. What colours your perception at any given moment in time in any situation? The colour of your perception is determined by the way you may feel at the moment you are being confronted with a particular situation. This is how your perception gives shape to the reality of your life.

> *Sometimes a simple change in the perception of your current circumstances can alter the course of your destiny.*

Just as one particular situation or behaviour can be perceived in multiple ways, the same situation or behaviour may not be perceived at all. Going back to the case study of the thirty-nine-year-old mum, she did not perceive that it was her self-destructive thoughts and emotions that were the root cause of the tensions in her family. If the perception has no grounding in a person's experience, or if there is no recollection of a memory of that experience, the person may not understand this.

Any interpretation of a new, unfamiliar situation or circumstance is coloured by the mind's need to reach out for something that it already recognises or is familiar with. Your eyes, or any of the other senses, thereby give an interpretation of events that you haven't been able to comprehend as yet, based on that which is most closely related to an already known experience stored in the memory of your brain. This problem stems from the fact that humans are unable to understand new information without the inherent bias of their previous experience or knowledge. It is your previous knowledge that creates your reality of what is the truth and what is not. This is because the human mind can only contemplate that to which it can relate. As it is mentioned in the ancient Eastern philosophies:

> *It is not the eyes through which we see but the mind.*

During one of my first temple visits in India, I was quite surprised when I saw that these huge, magnificent elephants were tied only by a little rope to one of their front legs. I wondered why they just stood there and did not make any attempt to break away from the thin ropes to which they were tied. Later on I found out that when they were very young and much smaller, the same size rope had been used to tie them. Also, these young elephants were hit if they tried to escape. As they grew older and stronger, this memory stayed with them and this was enough to hold them back. They were conditioned to believe that they couldn't break away. A tiny rope and the fear of pain held them back so they never tried to free themselves. These animals could at any time break free from their bonds easily, but they didn't because they believed they could not.

I use this example here to emphasise how, like the elephant, your mind is tied up with the invisible rope of your past insecurities, anxieties and fears. Any sensory experience of the mind is based on those stored memories that then trigger you to act or respond in a certain way. However, if you go beyond the conditioning, the emotional trauma and fears, your mind is not like the compliant elephant but more like a wild horse, whose nature is to run freely, to expand, to explore beyond the fencing of its conditioning.

The nature of the mind is to explore beyond the fencing of its conditioning.

Although your mind loves to run fast, chasing wildly after one thought then one sensation, and then onto the next thought followed by the next sensation, it does not mean it can't slow down or even stand still. It is in the standing still of the mind where you gain access to the unconditioned, uncoloured, heightened awareness I talked about earlier. This is the doorway that provides access to that Matrix of improved health and wellbeing, your own inner self-healing mechanism. In the following chapters of this book you will find *Ayuwave's* practical, easy-to-incorporate tools that take the mind beyond its conditioning, where you will find the key to youth that will help you to improve your health and wellbeing.

> "It takes but one positive thought when given a chance to survive and thrive to overpower an entire army of negative thoughts."
>
> Robert H. Schuller

The only thing that is required to retrain your mind at this point is your intention and willingness to do so. Remember, by knowing what needs changing, you are already half way there. You might argue your point saying that you can't change the way your mind functions, or you have had this habit for a long time and it is difficult or impossible for you to change. But recent research on neuroplasticity conducted by the Department of Psychiatry, UCLA School of Medicine, USA, has revealed that as you develop new habits, you rewire your brain. This proves the ability of the brain to change, even in adulthood. Once you are able to water the seed of wellbeing, rather than focusing on disease, wellbeing will gradually become the experience of your life. Perhaps you might have failed in the past; why not make another attempt and try again? As a well-known saying goes, "Your attempt might have failed, but never fail to attempt". Are you ready to rewire your brain?

The Relationship Between Awareness and Health

Hopefully, by now you have a good understanding of awareness and we can now look at the role of awareness in regaining and/or maintaining health. Whenever the term awareness is used in this paragraph, I refer to it as awareness in its purest form – what I call uncoloured, heightened or extended awareness, which can be experienced when the mind is in its most natural state, the state of non-conditioning. Once you gain access to this neutral state of heightened awareness through the instrument of your mind, you gain access to the source of potential order and intelligence of any form or creation simultaneously, which I will go into greater depth about in the following pages.

Knowledge or intelligence of how to heal and repair lies in the uncoloured, heightened state of awareness, which can be accessed through the Matrix.

Remember the silent depth of the ocean provides the foundation of all waves. The knowledge or intelligence of all its different shapes and forms, its potential to rise and to take the form of a particular wave with a specific shape lies there at the bottom of the ocean. Similarly, the knowledge or intelligence of how to heal and repair lies in the uncoloured, heightened state of awareness.

This awareness, because it is intelligence, knows what to do when we fall sick or injure ourselves. Just think for a moment… When you cut your finger, do you need to consciously think of what to do for the tissue to repair? No, your body's auto immune response kicks in and knows exactly what to do. Once you cut yourself, your skin goes through a multi-stage process of regeneration. First, there's the inflammatory phase, when your skin goes into overdrive to prevent further damage; the blood vessels narrow and the blood coming out of the wound clots to stop the flow. Your body releases a flood of chemicals that start the healing process and specialised cells clear the wound of debris over the next few days until, eventually, a new layer of skin forms. This process of healing and repair happens in a silent and effortless way, without your conscious involvement in the process.

> *"There exists in every person a place that is free from disease, that never feels pain, that cannot age or die. When you go to this place, limitations cease to exist."*
>
> Dr Deepak Chopra

It was established in the early 1930s by Dr Royal Rife that every cell in the body vibrates at a certain frequency and that the bio-frequency of humans can be measured to determine the relationship between frequency and health or ill-health. For example, a healthy liver has a frequency of 55 to 60 hertz, the heart a frequency of 67 to 70 hertz and the normal brain frequency is 72 to 78 hertz. The human body has a normal frequency range of 62 to 68 hertz. Unhealthy lifestyle and eating habits (such as the consumption of coffee or alcohol) cause a drop in the frequency and this has an effect on the immune system. As established by Dr Royal Rife, if the body's frequency drops to 58 hertz, cold and flu symptoms start appearing, 55 hertz triggers diseases like candida and, at 52 hertz, Epstein-Barr virus. Cancer is at 42 hertz and below whilst death begins at 20 hertz.

The human body has a normal frequency range of 62 to 68 hertz.

Keeping the above in mind and knowing that the knowledge or intelligence of how to heal and repair lies in the uncoloured, heightened state of awareness, it can be inferred that this pure state of awareness has the frequency of perfect health. Even if the frequency has dropped to 42 hertz, the body's self-repair mechanism, when activated in the state of higher awareness, knows how much to raise the frequency so that normality can be restored. This way, it can be said that the heightened state of awareness is the source of perfect frequency; intelligence in action, which, when tapped into, restores health and wellbeing.

Therefore, for any healing or repair to occur, it is not the specific healing system, modality or procedure that is responsible for restoring normal health, but it is that uncoloured, heightened awareness that does the job. In my *Ayuwave* practice, all techniques and procedures are purely to provide a space for my clients so this awareness or the body's own innate healing intelligence can take over. I am not the one who does the healing; I simply facilitate the process.

> *Heightened state of awareness is the source of perfect frequency; intelligence in action.*

As you move through the various chapters of this book, you will be equipped with tools that help you to access heightened awareness, the Matrix which brings you improved health and wellbeing. This might sound difficult or complicated but the good news is, like anything natural, it does not require much effort; just a bit of discipline and trust in the process. As the personal trainer, Billy Beck III said, "Open minds open doors to the impossible".

Vedic Science – The Matrix to Heightened Awareness

For thousands of years, knowledge systems throughout the world have provided insights and answers as to how to maintain wellbeing, how to regain health as well as how to restore youth and vitality. My intention in this book is not to discuss which system is better and which might not be effective. Over several decades I have tried to find the perfect answer and experimented in many different ways until I found out what has turned my health and, because of that, my life around. This book is the result of this exploration and, as a natural health practitioner, I can say with confidence that it has worked for me and for many of my clients.

If you are still holding this book in your hands after having worked your way through the initial abstract concepts, then this could be an indication that you resonate with what you have read so far. Perhaps some of the answers as to how to improve your health and wellbeing, how to maintain or restore youth, can be found in this book. In the end I trust your inner knowing, which will tell you exactly what is right or what might not be that suitable for you. This inner knowing and how it can be accessed is exactly what has drawn me to the ancient Vedic philosophy, which goes back thousands of years.

What is Vedic Philosophy?

The very word 'Veda' can be translated as 'knowledge'. Although the Vedas are considered the earliest literary record of India and the most sacred books of the Hindu people, the true experience of the knowledge of the Vedas won't be found in any book. The true knowledge of the Vedas unfolds on the level of heightened awareness, in a state of deep relaxation and meditation. This is where the ancient seers have perceived the knowledge of the entire Vedic literature, which has stood the test of time, and today can be seen as the source from which all philosophical maxims of mankind have emerged.

As is the microcosm so is the macrocosm.

There are many different branches of Vedic Science. However, I will concentrate only on those aspects that are most relevant and that need consideration when discussing health. All of them share the same perspective that the microcosm, you and I, even down to our cellular level, is a reflection of the entire universe – as above so below, as is the atom so is the universe, as is the human mind so is the cosmic mind. When trying to understand yourself, you have to see that you are a reflection of totality and you, in turn, contribute to that totality.

Again, using the analogy of the ocean and wave, each individual wave originates from the same source, the depth of the ocean. Similarly, all individual existence on this planet is an expression of the ocean of life, which is consciousness or awareness in its uncoloured, heightened state that has taken a specific colour, shape or form but, in essence, has no colour, shape or form.

Aspects of Vedic Science

Ayurveda – The knowledge of how to live a long and healthy life

Ayurveda is a system of health care originating from India thousands of years ago. It can be seen as the mother of all natural therapies. Ayurveda is a Sanskrit term derived from the roots, 'Ayus' meaning life and 'Veda' meaning knowledge. The tools for health and wellbeing as conceived in Ayurveda take a complex perspective, embracing body, mind and non-material explanations to align disjointed forces within an individual's physiology. Ayurveda considers nutrition, lifestyle and personal attitudes towards health as essential. Every aspect of one's health can be analysed through a sound understanding of one's natural constitutional makeup. The constitutional type of an individual can be seen through the lens of a five-element-theory. Similar to Chinese medicine, Ayurvedic medicine explores the composition of body-mind as permutations and combinations of the energies of space, air, fire, water and earth.

In the remaining chapters of this book, I use testimonials and case studies combined with my personal experience to discuss in much greater depth how I incorporate many of these time-tested principles and concepts of Ayurveda in my *Ayuwave* clinical practice today.

Jyotish – Vedic Astrology

This is an aspect of Vedic Science I am passionate about. I use Vedic Astrology in my clinic as a tool to promote positive health and wellbeing. My Vedic Astrology consultations are not designed to predict the future but to look into potential health challenges, to recognise imbalances of the physical as well as mental, emotional, energetic and spiritual bodies. In a Jyotish consultation, your chart, which is drawn up using your correct date, time and place of birth, is explained to you in detail. The Ayurvedic Astrology reading can offer a better understanding of your full potential, with personalised solutions to health challenges. It can also help unveil a hidden talent or dormant skill that could be the key to greater fulfilment and happiness in life, as well as obstacles and how best to manage their influences.

Vastu – Vedic Architecture

This is India's ancient Vedic tradition of architecture and interior design, using natural principles to enrich human life and to improve the quality of living experience at home and at work. Whether we are at home or in the office, the environment we are in has a strong influence on how we feel mentally, physically or emotionally. Vastu provides guidelines on how to create a supportive environment that will enable you to get in touch with the state of heightened awareness and which helps you to unleash your inner potential so you can improve your health and wellbeing. Vastu refers to the structure of your home as a representative of your own body.

Although I am not going to discuss the principles and concepts of Vastu in this book in great detail, I would like to share how healthy, uplifted, energetically charged and calm I felt when I lived and taught for a six week period at an institute in Japan. The building was purpose-built in alignment with cosmic forces. It is something that can't be described in words but must be experienced. Also, during the bushfires in California in 2003, 800 homes were destroyed but the fire passed right around six homes within the community that were built according to Vastu.

Gandharva Veda – Vedic Knowledge of Music and Sound

'Gandharva Veda' is the eternal music of nature, used to create balance in nature and to support inner peace and wellbeing. It uses sound, melody and rhythm to restore balance and harmony in mind, body, behaviour and environment. There are specific patterns of notes that are played with reference to the divisions of time during the day, based on the movements of the sun.

In the early 1950s, Dr Singh of the Department of Botany at Annamalai University, Madras, India, discovered under his microscope that plant protoplasm was moving faster in the cell

> *"Gandharva Veda is the music of nature, which inspires and promotes evolution. Gandharva Veda produces the influence of harmony in one's environment, which creates a harmonious influence in the field of consciousness, purifying and nourishing the environmental trends."*
>
> *Maharishi Mahesh Yogi*

as a result of the sound produced by an electric tuning fork. This discovery led to his conclusions that sound must have some effect on the metabolic activities of the plant cell. Inspired by these results, Dr Singh began a series of experiments on different plants where for several weeks, just before sunrise, he played to these plants specific melodies related to the natural vibration of the time of the day. From the results of this experiment, he concluded that Gandharva Veda sound waves affect the growth, flowering, fruiting and seed-yields of plants.

Once I learned of this experiment I was keen to try it out on a much smaller scale. For a period of several months I played Gandharva Veda melodies on a twenty-four hour repeat modus to my plants in the living room at home. The volume was turned down to almost silent so that it did not interrupt my life at home. To my surprise I could see, after some weeks, the plants that were exposed to the Vedic sound waves had flourished whereas the others did not. Even the branches of the plants in the living room started to lean in the direction of the speakers. The difference was very noticeable in comparison to those plants on the windowsill in the study room next door, with the same size window and facing in the same direction. When visitors asked me what I did to my plants to make them look so healthy I answered, "They listen to music all day long".

Vedic Approach to Health

> "We are not human beings having a spiritual experience. We are spiritual beings having a human experience."
>
> *Pierre Teilhard de Chardin*

When considering any holistic approach to health and wellbeing, it would be foolish to take a microscopic view, which examines only what goes on physically. The definition of holistic health is all-inclusive and considers the health of body, mind and what can be called spirit or soul. It is your overall state of wellness on all levels of your being: physical, emotional, mental and energetic. It encompasses the health of your entire being and extends to everyone and everything that affects you in any way. That includes your resources, your relationship towards yourself, your level of happiness and fulfilment in life, your environment and your relationships.

Holistic health is inclusive and considers the health of body and mind and beyond.

The Vedic approach to health is a holistic model that I use at various stages in my *Ayuwave* clinical practice, not only to improve the physical sense of wellbeing of my clients, but more so it provides an invaluable tool to create harmony and balance on all the subtler bodies. The techniques, principles and procedures used in my clinical practice are based on Vedic Science and are carefully selected, depending on each client's needs to help shift their awareness from the limited, individual self to the extended, unconditioned higher self. This then provides an ideal environment for the body's own inner self-healing mechanism to kick in, where improved vitality and regained youthfulness can then be observed as a pleasant side effect.

Oneness as the Matrix to Youth

The purpose of Ayurveda is to add years to your life and life to your years. How would you define life? For some it could mean being able to travel to remote places and continents; for others it could be having a good meal or an inspiring conversation. Ayurveda defines life as 'the harmonious interaction of the body, senses, mind and soul'.

Ayurveda adds years to your life and life to your years.

Let's look a bit closer at the meaning of each aspect. Your physical body is a field of molecules that combine together in a particular way to form your physique. Your body is tangible matter. The mind is a buzzing field of ideas informed by sensory experience. The mind is also a place where thoughts arise. There are thoughts that are more dominant than others. Nevertheless, the very fact that you perceive them means that they are in principle energy and information. The spirit or soul is that which orchestrates the activity of the energy and information (mind/senses) and the molecules (body).

A harmonious integrated functioning of your body, mind, sense and soul is a natural process. There is no difference between the functioning of the human body and the organism of the universe; the silent force of nature governs both. In a quiet, perfectly organised and systematic manner the moon moves around the earth, the earth around the sun. Cycles of day and night come and go in perfect order. Things go wrong when we interfere with this natural process; take the example of the effect the deforestation of the Amazon rainforest has on climate changes. Interference on a physiological level comes due to the stress it places on systems. Stress produces free radicals in the body, which are molecules known to be responsible for tissues damage and declined youthfulness.

Stress is the cause of declined youthfulness.

Ageing and anti-ageing have become commercialised terms to sell products and services. I consciously choose not to use the term ageing because age has a negative connotation. Also it is a parameter that shapes and defines our society. How can we anti-age? From people, to trees, to wine and cheese, ageing is a normal biological process. A 150-year-old oak tree might perhaps become 200 years old, but even the best fertiliser won't transform that tree into a 100-year-old tree. There are so many terms associated with age; biological age, social age, physiological or chronological age. Some people might be aged forty but they look sixty or vice versa. Age can be very confusing and you may not want to admit that you do age; yet it haunts you at the dawn of every new day when you wake up and look in the mirror. So I prefer to use the term 'youth' or 'restoration of youthfulness'.

As we have established above, a decline of youth is due to stress. Stress is a known major contributory factor in many disease processes that might affect you, from heart disease and cancer to anxiety, depression, addictions, sleep and relationship problems, and cellular degeneration.

Telomere length – the marker to measure youth

According to science, stress appears to influence the rate of telomere shortening, which is now being recognised as an important indicator or marker in measuring youth. Telomeres are microscopic caps that protect the ends of our chromosomes. These little collections of DNA are involved in a vitally important process of cellular division that helps our bodies to function normally. Each time a cell divides, we lose a portion of this telomere cap, which becomes shorter. When the telomere shortening reaches a certain critical length, cell division ceases. Whilst the cell remains alive, it can't renew itself and the ability to function slows or ends completely. These effects of shortened telomeres are known to cause diseases normally associated with loss of youthfulness.

As a result, scientists have been looking for ways to prevent telomeres from shrinking. In our clinic we use a specific blood test that is able to measure the length of telomeres not only to assess your biological age but also to monitor the progress of your journey towards improved health and wellbeing. So far, the best results appear to be through lifestyle changes, and at the top of this list is stress management. More stress means shorter telomeres, which in turn create less effective cells throughout the body. Simply put, cells become old before their time as a result of repeated bouts of unmanaged stress.

The answers to this you hold in your hands. The *Ayuwave* self-help tools, techniques and procedures described in the following chapters help you to better manage stress, which will allow you to keep a macroscopic view of whatever goes on in your life. It will be the foundation for you to access the uncoloured, heightened state of awareness, a direct line to your doctor within, the Matrix to eternal youthfulness.

Restoration of youth is possible by re-establishing the connection to your higher self through changing your perception, which will automatically lead to increased awareness. It is that simple, as so beautifully summarised in the following quote by Rumi.

When you are in touch with that heightened state of awareness, not only will your doctor within tell you exactly what is good for you and what is not, but also in that state you have full access to altering your physiology towards perfect health. So remember, if you feel unwell or lack energy or vitality, you have just forgotten the telephone number of the doctor within. Increased awareness helps you to refresh your memory, to reset that intellect which has given you either the wrong phone number or perhaps has been the cause for you forgetting the number in the first place. No longer will you feel tempted to choose that food or particular lifestyle which is harmful to you and then convince yourself that what you do is actually useful. You will pick intuitively that which is supportive of your health, vitality and increased youth. Nature takes over quietly, with the least effort and time involved.

> *"I have lived on the lip of insanity, wanting to know reasons, knocking on a door. It opens. I have been knocking from the inside."*
>
> *Rumi*

Oneness in Time

Some people spend their whole lifetime trying to understand the concept of time. So in this section my intent is not to find the one answer; I leave that to the expert scientists and philosophers. However, whilst writing this chapter about awareness, it occurred to me how much awareness is influenced by time, and vice versa.

As time changes, awareness changes and as awareness changes, so does time.

Take for example the cycles of day and night which vary from person to person. For some of you, early morning is a time when your mind might be most alert and awake, especially after a good night's sleep. Whereas for others, this might be a time when it is hard to get the brain working; you might not be able to concentrate until about ten in the morning, and perhaps even then a cup of coffee is needed to do so. Here time influences your awareness.

Time is a concept that is perceived differently in different states of awareness.

On the other hand awareness can also influence time. For example, through the discovery of Ethernet, a global computer network technology which allows us to communicate faster and faster, an increased awareness of speed has very much influenced our concept of time. Awareness of the availability of electronic communication influences our concept of time. We need to move faster, do things faster; yet we seem to have less and less time. We should be able to save time. Why don't we do that? Is it because our awareness is in a fast speed mode that has

> "The secret about time is that it exists only as we usually think of it. Past, present and future are only mental boxes for things we want to keep close or far from us, and by saying that 'time flies,' we conspire to prevent reality from coming too close. Is time a myth we are using for our own convenience?"
>
> Dr Deepak Chopra

changed our perception of time? If that is the case, is time real or is it something society has created?

The Misuse of Time

When I was nine years old I was given an expensive watch by my godfather. I have hardly worn it and strangely enough I haven't bought a watch myself in my entire life. Even long before the age of mobile phones I never felt tempted to carry time with me in the form of a watch. And looking back, I can say that I still managed to get around mostly on time even without the time. Time is such a peculiar thing. When you want to find out about the current time you are already in the past and trying to read the past time when you are far into the future. What I am trying to say here is that time can't actually be chased. However, when reflecting on the past thirty years or so, society has become more and more dependent on time. Everything is measured in time. The race against time has become the driving force of our life.

Think about this: when there are tasks ahead of you that you enjoy doing and derive pleasure from, you can always make the time to complete them, irrespective of how busy your day might be. This time is the right time… On the contrary, if there are things that you dislike or feel uncomfortable dealing with then you are using time, or the lack of it, as an excuse not to complete them. This time is not a good time.

There are also moments when there appears to be no concept of time, mostly perhaps in the state of meditation. Five minutes can feel like an hour and an hour can feel like five minutes. What is this about time? Why does the availability of time or lack of it, 'the right time' or perhaps 'the not so right time', so much depend on the way you feel or on your emotional response to life's circumstances? Are you not making yourself a victim of time?

Especially in moments when you reflect on the events of the day, don't you often feel guilty because you may have misused time? You have convinced yourself that it is alright to procrastinate, yet you feel anxious about your future, perhaps replaying your past behaviour and neglecting the 'now' to anticipate what is ahead of you tomorrow. You race through your life without appreciating the world around you in the 'now'. Time is such a subjective experience that by trying to find 'the right time' to do what we have to do is like waiting for three weeks of sunshine in Britain. There is no point in trying to find the right time because time is never actually right. The only thing that is there is the 'now'. Don't resist change; don't wait for the right moment to take responsibility for your health because the perfect moment is right in front of you, it is here in the 'now'.

We can't change the past, but we can influence the future by taking control of the present.

I don't know how long I stood there. We both seemed to keep staring at each other. At some stage I spotted a stranger walking down the path, confidently marching towards the black snake, stepping on it and greeting me with a "Gidday mate..." whilst walking past. It was only then that I noticed the assumingly dangerous snake turned out to be a curled up rotten branch of wood.

What created the snake in my mind? Was it the colour of the wood and the way it was laying on the footpath in a coiled shape that created the snake? Or was it my awareness, my anxiety, that had increased after finding out that Australia has the most poisonous snakes in the world that influenced my perception and made me view the wood as a snake?

What If

- What if you had the tools to change your awareness so you are able to see reality as it truly is, not as you have accepted it to be, because of your upbringing, education and life's circumstances?

- What if by changing the quality of your awareness you could change the quality of your life towards better health and wellbeing?

- What if you acquired the skills to access the Matrix to youthfulness?

Calls to Action

The Rice Experiment

Place one cup of cooked rice into two separate glass jars. Close the lid.

Mark one container with a positive phrase: "You are beautiful – I love you".

Mark the other container with a negative phrase: "You are ugly – I hate you".

Place them in your kitchen at least 20 centimetres apart.

Once or more every day say aloud to the rice container the phrase written on it. Try to say it from a place of gratitude (I love you) and a place of anger and frustration (I hate you).

See what happens to the rice in the different containers after a couple of weeks.

Attention

Begin your journey to improved health and youthfulness by sitting quietly, with your eyes closed, for a minimum of ten minutes on a daily basis. Put your attention to your heart and ask yourself:

What does being healthy mean to me?

How would I feel if I had more energy, better quality of sleep, improved digestion and so on?

Choose a day where you pay attention to how time passes. Take a piece of paper and write down, based on your activities of the day, when time appeared to move faster and when time did not seem to move at all.

Reflect on how your state of mind, emotions and physical state has influenced your perception of time.

Amrita – Nectar of the Natural Health Matrix:

- A heightened state of awareness is the state where you can access your Natural Health Matrix.

- Change your perception to change your health.

- Restoration of youth is possible by re-establishing the connection to your higher self.

- Stress is the decline of youthfulness.

TWO ~ EARTH

Key Concepts Of Ayurvedic Health

Pristine white gloves, austere-looking and short, dressed in a perfectly fitted and ironed navy blue uniform, struggling to prevent his cap from slipping over his eyes. Like some kind of 'Ghostbuster', he was operating a back mounted vacuum cleaner, the weight of it obviously challenging his balance. The smell was rather unusual, perhaps artificial, and it reminded me of a dusty pine forest.

One could picture this scene easily in the lobby of a five-star hotel, but in a car park at the airport in the world's most populous city? As my travel companion and I were driven through the busy city, with hardly an exchange of words, a magnificent landscape magically unfolded in front of us, telling its own story. After a seemingly endless drive, leaving the stunning Lake Chuzenjiko behind us, we finally arrived at the Vedic centre, totally secluded in dense mountainous forest in Nasu district, Tochigi, North of Tokyo.

As I got out of the car and woke up to the beauty of my surroundings, my jaw dropped as my eyes fell upon something beyond my imagination: a perfectly symmetrical building fanned out in front of me in the form of an ancient one-storey Japanese palace, built entirely out of wood.

The moment I entered the building with its perfectly symmetrical shapes and forms, a geometric courtyard at the epicentre seized my attention. I was mesmerised. Designed to absorb positive energy and distribute it throughout the building, I felt the powerful balancing force of this extraordinary construction.

For the first time in my life I was overwhelmed by the noise of silence. It was so still that the inaudibility screamed at me; a total awakening through the aural nothingness accompanied by a tingling sensation throughout my body. I was completely lost. It was as if I had my hands glued to an electric fence, electrocuted by the intensity of silence; an uneasy paradox of 'uncomfortable and blissful'. Other-worldly. Beyond the physical body, consuming. Instead of feeling relaxed as I had imagined it would feel, this 'perfect' home, built in alignment with the principles of nature, served to build a dominating, painful tension within me. I tried desperately to control the feeling. The more I tried, the greater the pressure in my head built. For the first couple of nights I could not sleep. I developed crushing headaches to the extent that I was unable to teach an afternoon session because I had to lie down, struggling with a migraine. What was going on here? I knew I wasn't getting a bug. Could a building really trigger these experiences?

In This Chapter We Discuss:

- the importance of familiarising yourself with the parts of Ayurveda that build the whole of health and wellbeing
- optimal learning and the state of least resistance
- your Ayurvedic constitution
- the nature of metabolism
- finding your individual rhythm

Why is This Chapter Called 'Earth'?

Whilst the first chapter looked at space as central to change, this chapter is connected to the most basic of the elements, 'earth'. Although from the perspective of the evolution of elements, earth is the last to manifest, from the perspective of what forms the foundational basis of all that exists, earth is like the building blocks of creation. It's like the pieces of Lego that you can put together to create a structure that you had in mind, so this chapter introduces you to the building blocks of Ayurvedic principles that in turn will assist you in creating the perfect health for which you have the potential.

The Need to Lay the Foundation

Think about a situation, one where you chose to rush to get things done quickly. And when for some reason you unexpectedly had to slow down, you may have realised that exactly that situation has helped you to get the essence and a better understanding of what needed to be

> "A successful man is one who can lay a firm foundation with the bricks others have given him."
>
> David Brinkley

done. As a result of that you might have been more productive with less effort. On the other hand, picture yourself trying to operate a computer without spending the time to study its software manual; you may feel frustrated and ready to give up before you actually have started.

Well begun is half done.

So this chapter lays the foundation for your ability to make full use of the information contained in this book as you discover your unique *Natural Health Matrix*. You may feel confident thinking that you are ready to race ahead, perhaps because you have read already about the principles of Ayurveda in other books, or you may think *I will figure it out along the way.* Although this might very well be the case, I would still encourage you to slow down and make the effort to study the following pages.

A Vastu home is designed through careful consideration of each step of the construction process. From the initial conceptual stages in the minds of the owners, to the actual architectural design of the building – with

> *"Get to know the parts to create the whole."*
>
> Aristotle

precise measurements such as the heights of ceilings, the width of the corridors, the exact time when the foundational stone must be laid, the building material that is being used – to the actual completion and the timing of inauguration of the building, the whole build is carefully orchestrated.

Taking Aristotle's saying, "Get to know the parts to create the whole," I would say that you can only fully comprehend Ayurveda's potential in creating health and wellbeing when the relevance of each key principle has been understood fully. This is when Ayurveda is not just an interesting, philosophical knowledge but when it can help you actually to transform your life.

'The whole' represents higher awareness; 'its parts' are the principles and concepts of Ayurveda. These building blocks when put together create something much bigger than when left on their own. When put together, they will grant you naturally access to a heightened state of awareness, where you will be able to unveil the Matrix, which will guide you on your journey towards health and wellbeing. However, this can't happen without familiarising yourself with those parts or building blocks. Surrender to the process and you will be surprised how effortlessly the Matrix will unfold in front of you.

The State of Least Resistance

Perhaps you may find it difficult to accept that the way a building is constructed would allow you to hear the silence or might be the possible cause of a migraine attack. What about this: when studying or reading a book whilst facing one direction you may fall asleep; however, when turning around 180 degrees, staying alert might be most natural.

A recent development in neuroscience, leading to an article published in 1996 in *Brain Research Bulletin 40,* has now confirmed the ancient understanding that our brain is sensitive to orientation, position and direction in space. Scientists were able to measure very accurately how well the brain functions under different conditions. In summary, the firing rate of specific neurons in the thalamus changes to the direction in which the head moves; our brain seems to function optimally when facing towards east.

The complexities of interferences in our environment, especially in today's electronic world, whether consciously or subconsciously experienced, often knock us off course and are a leading cause for many imbalances. On the other hand, a calm, serene and peaceful environment, symmetrically aligned, allows us you to tap into an energy that has been blocked by overwhelming external stimuli.

You may not be able to build the ideal home or re-arrange your existing living space, but if during the next pages you feel like drifting off, or if you are very likely to fall asleep, how about getting your compass out and aligning yourself so you face east. This provides you easier access to your heightened state of awareness, where resistance to learning is minimal and receptiveness to new concepts and principles is highest.

Key Concept 1: Definition of Health in Ayurveda

Think about this: if you are part of the National Health System and you have money taken automatically out of your salary, do you get your money's worth? What about the long waiting lists, basic treatments and doctors who are under stress because of long hours and lack of time?

Or if you have a health insurance, just reflect on the following for a moment:

- How much money have you invested to date in your health insurance?
- How much more money do you still have to pay until you leave this planet?
- How much extra money have you already invested to pay for services that are not covered by your insurance such as drugs, glasses and dental services?

Your biggest asset is your health.

As the philosopher Voltaire said, "In the first half of our lives we sacrifice our health to earn money; in the second half we sacrifice our money to regain health". In a society where being sick is getting more expensive and staying healthy is almost becoming a luxury, think carefully when it comes to investing in your health.

Interestingly, the definition of health according to the World Health Organisation is very much in line with the Ayurvedic philosophy;

"Health is a state of complete physical, mental and social wellbeing and not merely the absence of disease or infirmity." WHO, Definition of Health

However, when it comes to health, modern medicine is primarily focused on the treatment of diseases. Ayurveda is prevention-oriented and aimed to preserve health and wellbeing.

Health is an interaction between the external and the internal environment. External factors are triggers and internal factors respond to the trigger; therefore, building inner strength is essential in as much as changing the external environment is. In conventional medicine, drugs are developed based on the concept of eradicating and eliminating microorganisms, which are seen as the cause of ill health. In Ayurveda, a disease is the product of an imbalance of physical, mental, emotional and energetic elements, which leads to a reduction in the body's ability to fight disease. Ayurvedic herbal formulas, lifestyle changes and diet help to build inner strength and thus the body's immunity to eliminate disease or illness.

Health is an interaction between external and the internal environment.

In Ayurveda the mechanism of the interaction between the external and the internal is explained in the framework of four aspects:

- the three bio-energies or Doshas, a combination of the five elements that influence our body – space, air, fire, water and earth – responsible for movement processes such as circulation, transformation and digestion of food and the structure that holds your body together
- Agni – metabolic processes
- the seven bodily tissues called Dhatus
- its waste disposal system – Malas.

Ideal Health in Ayurveda is:

- when the three bio-energies are in balance
- when your metabolism is normal; when food is completely digested and properly broken down in its nutrients; when these nutrients then are fully absorbed and readily integrated into body tissue
- when your waste disposal system is efficient to eliminate any unwanted toxic debris
- when you are in touch with your heightened state of awareness
- when your mind is steady, calm and strong.

Don't allow your health to become the luxury product of tomorrow; start taking responsibility for it today.

What if:

- there is a health approach with the main focus on prevention?
- you were shown a way to take charge of your own health?
- there is a cost effective health care system, which provides you with tools where you can call upon your doctor within?

There is an answer to these questions, and the answer is 'Ayurveda'

> ### *Call to Action*
>
> Find a quiet moment, sit down and reflect quietly on what 'ideal health' would mean to you.
>
> Write down three to five of your immediate health goals and one by one spend a couple of minutes to tune into your perfect state of wellbeing. Only move on when you feel the cells of your physical body have integrated your newly generated vibration of wellbeing. An indicator could be a deep sense of ease, inner peace and happiness or perhaps total relaxation.

Key Concept 2: Your True Nature – Your Constitution

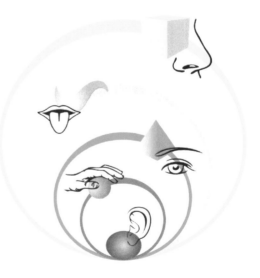

In order to call a system holistic it has to acknowledge that health is not just restricted to physical, mental or even emotional health. It goes beyond the 'you' and takes into consideration the relationship of the 'you' with its immediate environment and the entire universe. All existence in its entire complexity and diversity is nothing more than a manifestation of a single energy and intelligence. Ayurveda explains how this intelligence expresses itself through the five senses – hearing, touch, sight, taste and smell – which then give rise to the five elements – space, air, fire, water and earth. In simple terms, sound is perceived through the sense of hearing which forms the element of space. The skin allows us to experience the sense of touch, which gives rise to the element of air. It is through the eyes that we see that which forms the element of fire. Water relates to the sense of taste, which is perceived through the tongue. Earth is related to the sense of smell and the nose is the sense organ through which we perceive smell.

In all material existence, from the more dense to the most subtle, from a solid, heavy rock to the delicacy of an airy dandelion, these elements form a dynamic dance to create the world around us and our very own existence.

1. *Akasha-Space: The Silent Void of Creation*

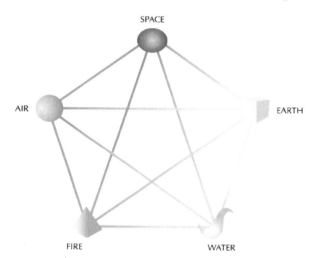

Akasha in Sanskrit means 'space'. The element space is symbolised by a point, the beginning and end of all manifestation. The colour usually associated with space is black. Space has been described as infinite and endless, into which all things lose their distinction. Similarly all colours, all light, lose their distinction in black. Sometimes the colour of indigo is also associated with space. It is also the colour that symbolises spiritual awareness, the key to the realm of the unknown, the Matrix of natural health.

In Sanskrit every word contains its own respective form. The sound created when pronouncing the word 'Akasha' is expansive. It can evoke feelings of liberation and freedom, where the boundaries that separate inner space from the outer dissolve. This sound is the primordial, omnipresent 'blueprint' of all existence. Just as the colourless sap of a plant contains the form of the entire tree, the sound of Akasha is the transcendental, eternal source of all energy, holding in its eternal stillness the infinite possibilities of life.

In Ayurveda, space is the container of all physical structures where life resides. Akasha embraces the co-existence of opposites within the void. This can be understood as the void being the field from which everything manifests and into which all eventually dissolves. Akasha has no beginning and no end; it is directionless and yet is the source of all directions. Akasha gives life to and nourishes the other elements. It provides the foundation for air, fire, water and earth to perform the dance of creation.

2. *Vayu-Air: The Invisible Force of Change*

Vayu is the Sanskrit term for 'air'. Air is the all-pervading element and is usually represented by a circle and the colour blue. The circle is a symbol of completeness and the colour blue of the immense sky. The white or silver of the element water and the blue of air are sometimes interchanged.

Like the wind, air is responsible for movement and change. Air is one of the subtle elements that cannot be seen but whose presence is felt by its actions. Try to catch air and you get a handful of nothing; it comes from nowhere, yet it exists everywhere–the uncontrollable which controls all.

Awareness rises out of the midst of the unknown through the element of air, giving birth to all material creation. Air does not belong to you any more just like your thoughts, which are ever evolving, they come and go. Your thoughts skip through your mind, like the wind brushing though your hair inviting you to follow and play.

Air as an element in Ayurvedic terms translates as a flash of inspiration and creativity. It is the fresh breeze of reason that makes thoughts come and go in a silent manner. Air is the brilliance of a genius or the restless agony of a mind in torment. Air is the conductor of the orchestra of time and is vital in making each instrument or element move. In the same way as hot particles of sand dance in the air following the call of the wind, constantly changing the landscape, air is in charge of the coming and going of thoughts. New ideas and thoughts form, and old ones disappear into the void.

Ayurveda understands the manifestation of air as the worries and sorrows of the mind; it is flexibility in motion, quick and alert. When held, compressed into pockets of water and earth, it can lead to an explosive reaction. Similarly, an overloaded mind, pushed down by the weight of thoughts, may give rise to a headache. Air and mind alike are born to be free and continuous. A cool breeze of air when touching your skin can leave you feeling alert and clear. Equally, air has the power to provoke the waters of the ocean to rise as tidal waves, to dry out a lake or turn fire into a blazing fury.

3. Tejas-Fire: The Burning Flame of Desire

The Sanskrit term, 'Tejas' denotes the element of fire. Red is the associated colour for fire in Ayurveda and it represents Tejas. Fire and heat suggest life and therefore appear to be related to the life-giving colour of blood. The movement of a flame is generally upwards and it tends to form a point; hence a triangle is used to represent fire. A triangle can be perceived as strong as in the form of a pyramid. However, when unbalanced, as in a three-legged stool, some degree of control is needed to remain in harmony. Fire is unpredictable. Fire is used to cook our food and so sustain life; but out of control, the same fire can burn down the house.

Sun is fire, the Tejas of the universe, the penetrating heartbeat of creation that ensures life and brings light. It is the sun's mass that keeps all planets on their paths. Similarly, it is the dynamic flame within that makes us move with purpose, jump with joy and love with passion.

Fire needs air to sustain it. In Ayurveda air is considered as thought, whilst fire can denote desire. Like as a tender candle in the wind may struggle to stay alight, too many thoughts can overload our system and extinguish any desire. On the other hand, it is the dynamic interaction between air and fire which sparks our mind to initiate the action necessary for the fulfilment of our goals. Fire can alter the balance of nature. It can bring harmony or destruction. When shaken, the latent fire in the centre of the earth can erupt into a volcano, bringing a natural disaster. Likewise, an uncontrolled expression of hate or anger can produce the poisoned arrow that breaks someone's heart.

Transformation is the essence of fire. In fire even the hardest metals melt and change to ash. Fire is like a lamp that shines in two directions – creation and destruction. Deep inside its liquid nucleus the earth bubbles with fire, forever creating as it destroys. Fire is creation. It ignites from a minute spark, impulsive and overwhelming like a sudden burst of desire, which burns and can destroy if it is allowed to grow into a blaze. In contrast to air, fire has direction and determination, moving up in a triangular shape that is sustained as an equally steady energy whichever way the triangle is tipped. Of all elements, fire is by far the strongest, the most directional and yet the least predictable energy. Fuelled by the creativity of air, the flames of fire can increase, necessitating the grounding element of earth in order to be restrained.

4. Jala-Water: The Refreshing Spring of Emotion

The Sanskrit term for water is 'Jala' and is represented by white or silver and the shape of a crescent. Sometimes silver is replaced by blue. This is understandable as water appears blue when the sky is reflected in it.

Water is cool, refreshing and cleansing. It is fluid and wet. It represents our feelings and emotions. Water is grace in motion. It takes the shape of whatever contains it. Water, the sparkly juice of life, can ascend through a spring, like bubbles of bliss that arise effortlessly from the depth of our being.

Water also seeps through the cracks of the earth to quench the thirst-parched land made infertile by fire and air. Water can't be held in our hands; it slips through our fingers like thoughts and feelings leaking through the permeable membranes of our cells. Feelings can be as subtle as a gentle ripple on a silvery lake or as rough as a tidal wave destroying all in its path.

Water, like a foggy mirror, can reflect the subconscious instincts of our past and the conscious needs of our future. Water purifies; its force and power can cleanse the stains of the past as it washes away deeply engraved emotions from our soul.

Ayurveda understands the element of water as representing emotion. We cry tears of sorrow and of love. Because of its fluidity, water is an unstable element, the bringer of life or the destroyer. The winds of air make water rise or fall. The dryness of earth swallows its drops. Water evaporates in the heat of fire and then vanishes into the void of space until it is reborn as the tears of the sky. Water is the liquid moon that climbs slowly to claim the dark sky. Its cyclic nature beats the drum of time; it comes and goes, rises and falls.

5. Prithivi-Earth: The Eternal Pillar of Stability

The Sanskrit term for the earth element is 'Prithivi'. The colour yellow and the shape of a square represent earth. A square has four sides and is therefore perfectly balanced, suggesting stability. Similarly, yellow is the most frequent colour used to represent affluence. The precious metal gold and the medicinal spice turmeric, both from the earth, have yellow in common.

The element of earth brings reliability, stability, re-assurance, strength and comfort. It very much represents the ground we stand on and, in Ayurvedic terms, the strength and building blocks of life as well. Archaeologists reveal the history of time in their excavations; each layer representing a civilisation that came before. Similarly, we can build layers that represent a time and phase of our life, long since gone yet not forgotten. In most indigenous cultures, earth represents mother, the one who nurtures, supports and who preserves life.

These nurturing and supportive aspects can be equated with love. In a similar way to roots beneath the surface of the earth breaking through concrete, it is love that can break through resistance. Earth is supportive of life; it represents love, which accommodates all other emotions. Earth contains all the other elements and thus co-existence. Earth contains within it the necessary conditions for life on this planet.

> "The essence of the beautiful is unity in variety."
>
> W. Somerset Maugham

In its core it has water that erupts as springs and fire that can explode as a volcano, alongside channels of air created over aeons of time that now form fertile spaces for life to thrive. Earth is warm, protective and the preserver of life. It is the solidness of the future holding the salt of tears from the past. Earth needs water to prevent it from drying out and losing its fertility, but the balance is fragile. Too much water and earth becomes slippery, turning all into a river of mud. From an Ayurvedic point of view, water represents emotions; being too emotional can cause us to lose the stability beneath our feet.

Earth is essential for life but precarious. Excess heat and wind can dry earth to dust; the same dust can suffocate the flames of fire. Earth is the most basic of all the elements and in Ayurveda the one with least flexibility.

Five Elements Combined: The Three Doshas

When these elements combine they form the three Doshas, vital bio-energies that make up your human existence. They are:

1. Vata
2. Pitta and
3. Kapha.

They define your inborn tendencies that determine how you experience life. The three Doshas are the essence of who you are– your true nature and how you relate to your surroundings. It is your genetic code that usually does not change during your lifetime. A combination of space and air form the principle of Vata, fire and water make up Pitta and water and earth create Kapha.

If you fully understand your unique constitution and metabolic makeup, in a sense if you are aware of what are the predominant elements that govern your physical, mental and emotional being, then Ayurveda offers you a variety of tools to keep yourself happy and healthy by bringing these elements into balance.

Living in London may sound extremely daunting for some; but for me, at this moment in my life, it is one of the most fascinating cities I have lived in or visited. If you want to understand how all the elements translate into the shape and forms of a physique or behavioural patterns, with different looks and walks, then just sit down in the busiest areas of where you live and simply observe.

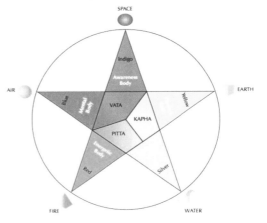

For me, the ideal place in London to observe others is the underground transport system, especially during rush hours. Everyone is united with one purpose, either to get to work on time in the morning or to get home as quick as possible at night.

Vata: A Combination of the Elements of Space and Air

VataQualities

- dry
- light
- cold
- rough
- subtle
- mobile

A Vata Constitution

Those who stand out in a crowd of people, those who are either very short or those who stick out like a sore thumb, are the Vatas. They are often very tall and thin with bony limbs, have long or angular faces with a small and narrow nose, tiny eyes that are sometimes sunken in and their lustre could be dull and pale. When shaking hands with a Vata, you may feel like you are touching a block of ice, as their extremities tend to be cold. They also have a tendency towards thin, dry and cracked skin.

Vata hair can be a challenge for any hairdresser as it is often dry, thin, frizzy and possibly curly. It doesn't fall into any shape naturally and, when styling, lots of fluffing up and products are needed to keep it in place.

A Vata Metabolic Type

Their appetite and digestion varies; sometimes they are hungry and other times they are not. This very much defines the nature of Vata – movement and change. Often with a Vata metabolism there are no rules about eating; you can eat at any time or can go on for hours without any food. They usually have no difficulties losing weight, but it may be hard for them to put on weight.

A Vata Personality

They get excited easily and, once they have finally made up their mind, they enrol in a Pilates class one day, do yoga the next and love dance the day after. Let a couple of weeks pass and they can't be bothered to do any of it. They just decide to stay home and listen to some music and perhaps write or paint.

Vata personalities think and act very quickly and can be very bubbly and lively. They are highly adaptable to change and usually flexible by nature, both mentally and physically. When practising yoga next to a Vata person you may feel jealous as they naturally tend to be very agile; however, their energy comes and goes in bursts and they usually lack stamina.

If you were one of those students who, whilst in college, studied frantically the day before the exam because you found any excuse not to start earlier, and by the time you got home in the afternoon you had forgotten most of what you had learned and what had been asked in the exam, you are definitely on the Vata side of life.

One of the greatest challenges for a Vata person is to learn to listen to others. But, on the other hand, they love to be listened to. When a Vata person sits in front of me in a consultation, I struggle to get a word in; they love talking. They keep me on my toes though, as I have to be fully present in order to be able to follow their speed in changing topics.

Vata people are always a good test for me to find out how connected I am to my higher self, especially when I am in a rush to get somewhere and they walk in front of me along Oxford Street. Oh dear, brace yourself when the wind blows into the fire… They walk left then suddenly change their course and jump to the right, just in front of me. I wish they would make up their minds so I could get past them. Never ever hand out your credit card to a Vata person. They tend to spend all of the money and come home with lots of bags, only to find out that what they actually were meant to purchase isn't there.

Vata – When Out of Balance

The above quote sums up the nature of Vata people when out of balance. They may sleep lightly and they often suffer from 'mental obesity' – a restless mind weighed down by its thoughts. Their sleep usually is interrupted and they often have difficulties falling asleep.

> "A ruffled mind makes a restless pillow."
>
> Charlotte Brontë

A Vata personality can be compared to the historic former East German 'Trabby' – a car that was designed to go comfortably at 90kilometres per hour. Pushing it to go faster on a permanent basis is the perfect recipe for a breakdown and a huge mechanic's bill. So is the constitution of Vata.

When a Vata person pushes too far, they will break down sooner or later. This can lead to insomnia, panic attacks, anorexia, constipation, hypertension, arthritis, weakness, restlessness and digestive challenges.

VATA						
Elements	**Qualities**	**Main System**	**Location**	**Traits**	**Tendencies**	
space air	dry light cold rough subtle mobile	central nervous system	region below the navel main seat: colon	creativity enthusiasm flexibility active alert	worries anxiety indigestion restlessness stress headaches	insomnia arthritis lower back problems dry skin poor circulation
TO LISTEN and TO LISTEN TO						

Pitta – A Combination of the Elements of Fire and Water

Pitta Qualities

- slightly oily
- sharp
- hot
- distinct smell
- fluid
- liquid

A Pitta Body Type

People with a dominant Pitta constitution naturally blend into the crowd. They are neither very tall nor on the short side. Usually, they have a moderate build and are easy to spot in a gym because they love showing off their well-toned and muscular bodies. A Pitta face often looks even with dominant features and a neat, pointed nose that is perhaps rather sharp. If you still struggle to imagine how a Pitta person looks, then you definitely will know when looking into their eyes. They are bright and may be light-blue, grey, hazel or copper-brown with an intense lustre. When they look at you, it almost feels as if they look through you with their intense 'x-ray' gaze. There is a tendency towards reddening of the whites of the eye and their teeth are medium in size and often yellow-coloured.

Pitta skin tends to be more reddish in tone, often with freckles and moles. When I was at college, I was teased not only because of my weight but also because I blushed easily; my face lit up like a light bulb. Luckily I no longer blush that easily and my skin is generally soft, lustrous and warm to touch. Probably because my Pitta is more under control today.

Hairdressers usually don't have problems with Pitta hair, especially with men because often there is not much to style. They have a tendency towards premature balding and early greying of hair. Their natural hair colour often has a reddish tinge and is soft and silky to touch.

A Pitta Metabolic Type

Usually a Pitta metabolism is excellent, which sometimes leads them to believe they can eat anything. They are unable to skip meals and need to have food at regular times. Often an hour after a main meal they are in the kitchen looking for food and they complain about feeling hungry again.

A Pitta Personality

They share a great passion for life. The character who describes some of the traits of Pitta best is Carmen, in the opera (of the same name) by the French composer George Bizet. Carmen is highly complex; intensely coloured with emotion and passion; full of complexity, mystery and internal contradiction.

Vata people have all the great ideas and brilliant imagination but it often ends there. Pitta personalities tend to be good leaders and they are brilliant managers who generally make decisions quickly. They will take the ideas proposed by Vata and work out plans, down to the finest details, that transform these ideas on paper into reality. They would even go as far as taking their laptop to the lavatory to plan and structure the project. They hold on to a task like a dog to a bone; they won't let go until they can celebrate its completion. They love to analyse and critically compare different options and their minds are brilliant, with a passion for details. They love arguments and to criticise others, but only invited criticism is welcome. The most challenging trip for them could be to travel from 'their head' to 'their heart'.

Pitta personalities have a brilliant sense of direction and often a photographic memory. When first moving to London, I made it a point not to take any map with me whilst exploring the city. As a result, within a short period of time I was able to find my way around. Even in school I learned by remembering where in a book a particular concept was, or where information had been explained. I then visualised that picture to recollect the information I needed during the exam.

> "The will to win, the desire to succeed, the urge to reach your full potential..."
>
> Confucius

In my clinic I take a different approach depending on the metabolic type that presents to me. When seeing a Pitta client I keep in mind their need to understand why they should do what I suggest them to do. They love lists and telling them "...take a handful of rice and boil in a cup of water..." won't be sufficient. For them the instructions would be,"... take 100grams of white, unpolished, organic basmati rice; wash thoroughly, at least three times; boil in 1 ½ litres of pure Kangen water in a saucepan with a capacity of 3 litres for at least two hours on number three..." I guess in that sense they can be very German...

Pitta – When Out of Balance

Pitta people, when out of balance, may have the tendency towards overheating, which could manifest in heartburn, acidity, diarrhoea and cystitis. They are usually more sensitive towards chemicals and food additives, leading to food allergies, digestive related headaches or migraine and skin problems.

Resentment, aggression and jealousy are common emotions that flare up when Pitta is out of balance. Often they are perfectionists and therefore could have a tendency towards obsessions and fanaticism. Generally, they fall asleep easily but then they wake up in the early hours of the morning and can't go back to sleep.

PITTA					
Elements	**Qualities**	**Main System**	**Location**	**Traits**	**Tendencies**
fire water	slightly oily hot bad smell fluid liquid	digestive system	region around the navel main seat: stomach and small intestine	passionate warm natured charming leadership entrepreneurship intelligent visionary	anger resentment impatience fanaticism inflammation ulcers diarrhoea
TO UNDERSTAND and TO BE UNDERSTOOD					

Kapha – A Combination of the Elements of Water and Earth

Kapha Qualities

- slow
- heavy
- stable
- soft
- cold
- oily
- sweet

A Kapha Body Type

A Kapha metabolic type usually possesses a larger body frame and well-developed physique with a broad and even expanded chest. Generally, they are blessed with stamina, resilience and good immunity. They stand no chance to win a sprint, but in a marathon they thrive because of their endurance.

Their face is characterised by its round shape, with dark brown or blue eyes. If you want to know how a Kapha type looks, just watch out for people with naturally long eye lashes and large, dark brown or blue eyes that provide you access to 'the depth of their soul'. Whenever they smile the whole room lights up because of their naturally white, even and strong teeth.

Typical Kapha skin feels velvety soft, slightly oily and smooth to touch. Kapha hair is thick and plentiful.

A Kapha Metabolic Type

Their metabolism is rather slow compared to Pitta, and they can go all day without any food. Hunger is not something a Kapha person experiences easily. Often they struggle with their weight to the extent that even looking at food makes them feel they have put on a couple of kilograms.

A Kapha Personality

I love observing a Kapha person walk, provided I am not in a hurry. They show a lot of grace in their movements, which is a pleasure to watch. Their soft, low voice and slower speech reflects their deep thinking and deliberate thought process' as a result they may not be the most inspiring people to talk to. A Kapha person reflects a lot and they take a long time when it comes to making decisions. Their sleep is usually very deep and long; they love sleeping in.

Kaphas are very likable because they are easy going, joyous hosts, good listeners and great peacemakers. If you are ever in need, the Kapha person in your circle of friends will never let you down. They are the first to be there when you are in need. Their mood and nature can best be explained using the example of an elephant; in fact, let me share something with you …

At the age of six or seven, I was out on a Sunday family trip to the zoo. We were standing there watching the elephant and one of my brothers, feeling bored at watching a slow moving animal, started to throw some dust towards it, trying to irritate the animal, when suddenly a big trunk reached over the tiny brick wall that separated the enclosure from the spectators and grabbed my mother's hand bag. I was in shock. I thought that this giant animal was going to grab my mum and throw her around, a little bit like Jane in the movie King Kong. I screamed, took the sand and threw it at the animal to rescue my mum. The zookeeper arrived quickly, not impressed with what had happened, but he managed to calm down the elephant and returned the handbag to my mum.

A couple of years later, I went to the same zoo on a school trip. With the memory of my previous elephant encounter I approached the elephant area carefully. At some point (I can't remember how it happened and it was all very fast) the elephant filled his trunk with water and sprayed it like a hose directly towards me. Could it really have been the same elephant?

Although Kapha people can be extremely tolerant, just like the elephant they can hold a grudge forever if you upset them. Their mind is steady, with a positive attitude, but they are not the fastest learners in school; however, whatever they have learned they will never

> *"Truly great friends are hard to find, difficult to leave and impossible to forget."*
>
> *G Randolf*

forget. Kaphas need encouragement to get moving because they don't like to move. They also have a tendency to become attached to things because they usually don't like change.

Kapha – When Out of Balance

Kaphas gravitate towards a build-up of excess weight, lymphatic congestion and fluid retention. When out of balance, Kapha people tend be lethargic, sleep excessively and they may suffer from depression. They are more likely to suffer from respiratory conditions such as allergies and asthma as well as metabolic disorders, for example, diabetes and obesity.

KAPHA					
Elements	**Qualities**	**Main System**	**Location**	**Traits**	**Tendencies**
water earth	slow heavy stable soft cold sweet oily	immune system	region: chest upwards main seat: stomach	compassion stability strength loyalty endurance	lethargy depression overweight asthma diabetes hypothyroidism
TO LOVE and TO BE LOVED					

Call to Action

Using Ayurvedic questionnaires when trying to identify your biological constitutional type can often be misleading and confusing. Strictly speaking, you have to answer the questions twice once from the perspective of how you were when you were young, and the second time keeping in mind your current state.

Nevertheless, I would like to encourage you to use the questionnaire in the appendix of the book and go through the exercise for now. This will give you an indication as to whether you tend predominantly towards Vata, Pitta or Kapha. If you want to know your true nature, it is best to consult an Ayurvedic practitioner skilled in using pulse analysis.

Key Concept 3: True Nature Vs Current State

Reading through the previous section and having done the questionnaire, you probably have realised by now that trying to identify your unique biological constitutional type is not as straightforward as it appears to be. Even after twenty-five years of experience, I am still in doubt sometimes as to what my true nature is. By true nature I mean Ayurvedic 'biological constitution or metabolic type' at the time of birth, which is very much influenced by the following factors:

- the date, time, place and season of conception and birth
- the state of health of your parents
- your genetic predisposition.

This unique or true nature changes in the course of your lifetime, based on your upbringing, education, environment and lifestyle, and has to be taken into account when doing an Ayurvedic assessment. This can often be a challenge, and a skilled Ayurvedic practitioner does not rely purely on one method of assessment. It is a combination of asking the correct questions, using pulse analysis and observational skills, perhaps Vedic Astrology and a good portion of intuition, all of which lead to a final determination as to your true nature versus your current constitution.

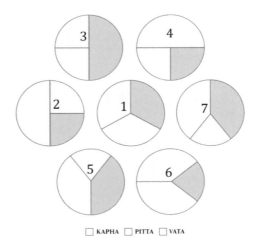

According to Ayurveda, pure awareness, as discussed in the first chapter, can manifest in the seven different body or constitutional types depending on the proportions of Vata, Pitta and Kapha:

1. Vata-Pitta-Kapha are present in equal proportions
2. Vata predominance with secondary Pitta and Kapha
3. Pitta predominance with secondary Vata and Kapha
4. Kapha predominance with secondary Pitta and Vata
5. Pitta and Vata predominance with least Kapha
6. Vata and Kapha predominance with least Pitta
7. Pitta and Kapha predominance with least Vata

See illustration above

Take the example of one of my clients, a forty-one-year-old male of medium build, slightly reddish skin with a well-toned muscular body and a sharp intellect who is highly success-driven, passionate in what he does and competitive in nature. Only when taking his pulse did I find out that there was underlying anxiety, fear, cracking joints and general dryness. He had also admitted his fear of failure and not to be accepted. Whilst assessing his true nature and present state I found out he had a genetic predisposition to diabetes, although at the time of the assessment his metabolism was excellent.

What would you say is the constitution of this person? Let's think about it. He is mainly Pitta as clearly seen through his external appearance and also most of his mental and emotional traits; however, there is also a strong presence of Vata, indicated by his anxiety. The genetic predisposition of diabetes is linked

to Kapha, so he belongs in the fifth category: Pitta and Vata predominance with least Kapha.

Keep in mind that just by looking at a person, it might appear from the outside that he or she may belong to one category; but don't get blinded by the external picture. Many people, including myself, are excellent actors, and when analysing someone's constitution there are often deeper, hidden elements that reveal the presence of one or two or perhaps all three bio-energies. And when missed, this can lead to a false interpretation.

In my practice, I have very rarely come across people who belong to the first category – equal proportions of Vata-Pitta-Kapha. But I must say that those few people I have seen were in excellent health and they have enjoyed a great sense of balance on all levels –physical, mental, emotional and on an energetic level, with a high degree of self-awareness.

When I talk about balance, I mean the correct proportions of Vata-Pitta-Kapha based on your true nature. This does not imply equal proportions. For example, you could be a predominantly Vata-Kapha personality with equal proportions of both, let's say, Vata 40%, Kapha 40% and Pitta could be present at 20%. The aim of Ayurveda is to bring your current state, which might be Pitta 50%, Vata 30% and Kapha 20%, back to the original state as described above.

Please don't get caught up in a mind game, especially if you gravitate towards the Pitta traits, thinking you need to figure out your exact percentages. Taking my personal example, when analysing my Vedic Astrology chart and when taking my pulse, my true nature seems to be more like Pitta predominance with almost equal proportions of Kapha, especially keeping in mind my mental and physical appearance about thirty years ago. Because of my lifestyle with lots of travelling, lack of rhythm in my life and a 'go, go' attitude, signs of Vata are definitely visible, manifesting as dry skin and disturbed sleep just to mention a few of them. I see a greater need to establish rhythm in my life than ever before to reduce the excess Vata and revert back to my true nature.

In essence, what I am trying to say here is that it is not just about shifting these bio-energies of Vata, Pitta and Kapha back to their original state. It is more important to get a sense of what balance means to you, so you will be able to make necessary corrections that help you to re-align your current state with your inherent true nature. This is a good start but not the end of your Ayurvedic journey. When working with my clients, I aim to also take into consideration factors, causes and events that could possibly have contributed to the fact that these bio-energies have become out of balance in the first place and how this has affected the subtler bodies.

Trying to identify someone purely by looking at the person can be misleading.

Call to Action

Reflecting on the above, taking into consideration your true nature versus your current state, just sit down and write down what 'balance' means to you and see if you can relate what you have written to one or two or perhaps all the three Doshic principles.

Key Concept 4: Revert to Your True Nature

Having established an understanding of the difference between 'true nature' and your 'current state', this section describes three principles which, when kept in mind, will help you to re-align with your 'true nature'.

These three principles are:

- Wherever there is smoke, there is fire.
- Like increases like.
- The principle of the opposites.

Wherever There is Smoke There is Fire

A twenty-eight-year-old mother saw me, complaining about excess heat, a burning sensation in the stomach, frequent headaches and loose bowel motions. The symptoms she presented with could easily be put into the Pitta category. However, when taking her pulse it was clear to me that her symptoms were simply a manifestation of an excess of Vata. You may ask, "Why?" In her case the Pitta symptoms can be compared to the smoke rising above the hill. But the question that needs answering is, "Where is the source of the smoke?" In her case it was the Vata – irregular sleep, poor nutrition and lack of rhythm in her life, where the burning fire at the bottom of the hill caused the smoke to rise. So by attending to the source, by helping her to find a rhythm in her life, to get some regular sleep and good nutrition, the fire stopped; there was no more smoke and all the symptoms improved.

In each case, the cause of any imbalance, where one has moved away from their true nature, will most likely be different. By aiming at finding out what is the cause that leads to the manifestation of the symptoms, you take your first step towards reversing your 'current state' to your 'true nature'.

The illustration below shows how the different elements can interact with each other. Each element, when out of balance, can be the cause of the problem or the symptoms that manifest as a result are the effect of it.

The wind – *cause* (Vata) blows into the fire – *effect* (Pitta).
Example: inability to handle stress could lead to heartburn or ulcers.

The heat of fire – *cause* (Pitta) dries out the air – *effect* (Vata).
Example: anger as the possible underlying cause for disturbed sleep.

The dampness of water – *cause* (Kapha) kills the fire *effect* (Pitta).
Example: excess fluid intake during meals is very likely to slow down your metabolic activity.

The heat of fire – *cause* (Pitta) burns up the earth – *effect* (Kapha).
Example: overactive metabolism could lead to emaciation or tissue depletion.

The earth – *cause* (Kapha) traps air – *effect* (Vata).
Example: toxins accumulated in small intestine could prevent nutrient absorption, leading to malnutrition.

Excess wind – *cause* (Vata) dries up earth – *effect* (Kapha).
Example: too much exercise could cause drying up of synovial fluid leading to joint problems.

Like Increases Like

Once we have established the cause of a specific problem by looking at the qualities of the element(s) that are responsible for the imbalance, we need to understand what would further aggravate the condition.

Let's take an example where too much exercise could be one of the possible causes for drying up of synovial fluid leading to joint problems. Excess exercise is an aggravation of Vata, the element of air. Anything that would further disturb Vata, such as a lack of fluid intake, excessive hot and bitter foods, or exposure to dry and cold winds, is very likely to further increase Vata, which in turn could worsen the joint problems and possibly bring about osteoporosis.

The Principle of the Opposite

Now that we know the cause and what could aggravate the symptoms of our 'current state', let's look at what to do to reverse the symptoms; to reverse the current situation and bring it back into balance. To do this I would like to share my own example. My 'true nature' according to pulse analysis and assessment of Vedic Astrology is Pitta-Kapha. My sleep used to be brilliant, deep and sound and it was often difficult for me to get out of bed in the morning. Perhaps because of extensive travel, living in hot and dry climates, too much mental activity and neglecting my creative nature during the past ten years, Vata has taken over, making my sleep extremely light. What helps me at night time is to apply oil to my feet, which calms down the mind and reduces the business of my brain. Oil is unctuous, warming and opposite to the drying and cold quality of Vata. It brings back the Kapha element, which reflects the actual me, giving me the patience, clarity and strength needed to deal with life's challenges. I will talk more about the benefits of oil massage in *Chapter Four – The Power of Transformation*.

This book is not aimed at self-diagnosis. In fact self-diagnosis can be potentially dangerous and I certainly do not encourage you to use the above three principles to treat yourself, especially when suffering from a serious condition. However, it will help you to increase your self-awareness by starting to analyse how the qualities of the five elements have influenced the way you think, feel or perhaps how your body functions. This allows you to make conscious choices. Naturally, you will start to know what is best for you and what perhaps should be avoided. You are in charge, so don't allow external influences to rule your life.

Call to Action

Analyse one or two of your current complaints in terms of its relation to the five elements and try to find out which element could be the underlying cause. Then think of what aspects of your life contribute to increasing the symptoms such as foods you eat and activities you undertake. Once you have identified these, write a list of things you can do that are the opposite, to counteract the effect.

For example, when my skin feels very cold and dry, this could be an indication of an excess of the element of air, so I introduce warm foods and use good quality oils such as coconut oil in my cooking and hemp seed oil when preparing food.

Key Concept 5: The Importance of a Healthy Metabolism

You are what you eat. Is this a myth, a fact or just an age-old saying? Does this mean that those who consume pork predominately look like pigs? And those who mainly eat what is considered healthy food would be healthy? Of course this adage should not be taken literally. No doubt what we eat affects the health of our body and mind, but the point I am trying to make here is a different one… Often, when I walk into 'Wholefoods' or the so- called 'health shops' and look around, I wonder why so many of the people who buy the 'best of the best' look so unhealthy, grey with no glow, thin and emaciated or puffed up and overweight.

Can you afford to flush your money down the toilet?

People purchasing supplements and health care products spend billions of pounds every year. According to a health care market research report (*Markets and Markets* 2010), the entire home health care market covered under the report is estimated to be approximately $159.6 billion; $143.1

billion in 2009, which is about 90% of the entire market. It is estimated to grow to $204 billion by 2014. So is it enough to spend all this money on health care and supplements to remain healthy? If that is the case, why is it that our society is becoming sicker and sicker? In my clinic last winter, I observed that when people came down with a cold or flu, the symptoms were worse and the time needed to recover was longer than it used to be. Not to forget the alarming rate of obesity worldwide. A lot of the money spent on supplements and healthy foods is simply flushed down the toilet because of your body's inability to decode the information in the supplement or food, so that it can be read and understood by the cells and used to build a healthy body.

The main key to perfect health is a healthy metabolism.

Irrespective of which Ayurvedic professional you consult, you will be asked questions about your digestion. Don't confuse good digestion with being 'regular'. You can have regular bowel movements but still have poor digestion. This book is not a textbook of Ayurveda, so in simple terms I would say that a healthy digestion is when the food you eat is properly broken down into its nutrients in the stomach, when waste is separated and these nutrients are then being fully absorbed into the blood stream via the small intestine and from there transported to the cells where they are utilised to form healthy tissues. In this section I will concentrate on the main digestive fire or 'Agni', which is responsible for the initial breaking down of food into its various constituents.

You can eat anything if your digestion is strong.

Agni: Digestive fire

'Agni' is a Sanskrit word meaning 'fire', which governs all chemical processes that occur within your body or on a cellular level that are responsible for the maintenance of life. In other words Agni is involved in the process of digestion and transformation, as well as in absorption and detoxification. It can manifest in your physiology as body temperature, digestive enzymes, amino acids and all metabolic activities. But Agni is much more than a biological or chemical action. According to Ayurveda your intelligence, your ability to connect to your higher awareness to understand

and comprehend, your sensory perception and longevity are also important functions of Agni. Agni as the main source of life works on many levels. It is also reflected in the radiant heat emanating from the sun as well as the dormant, latent heat in the centre of the earth.

Charaka, one of the ancient scholars of Ayurveda, commented 5,000 years ago that the root cause of any disease lies in an impaired Agni. If your Agni is healthy and strong, you can eat and digest anything.

An impaired digestion is the root cause of any disease.

EFFECTS OF COMPROMISED DIGESTIVE HEALTH	
hormonal imbalances such as hypothyroidism	*poor quality of sleep*
metabolic disorders such as diabetes and obesity	*ageing*
autoimmune disorders such as rheumatoid arthritis, multiple sclerosis	*hair loss*
	poor memory
	short attention span
food intolerances such as gluten and dairy allergies	*lack of energy*
aches and pains	*anxiety, anger, apathy*
	impatience
mineral and vitamin deficiencies	*lack of direction in life*
infections … etc. etc.	*poor circulation*
	visual problems

Types of Agni

In one of the previous sections I discussed that the five elements combine into the three bio-energies of Vata, Pitta and Kapha and they have their respective qualities. Vata is light, mobile, cold; Pitta is hot and sharp; Kapha is heavy, damp and solid. Agni by nature has its own qualities such as hot, sharp, slightly oily, light, dry and mobile. When you write the qualities of the three bio-energies and Agni down in a table and compare, you will probably realise that Agni has similar qualities to Vata and Pitta and that the qualities of Kapha are opposite to those related to Agni.

In order to understand the different types of Agni, let's have a look at some of its qualities and their effect when interacting with the five different elements. The space element allows fire to expand and to spread, as there are no boundaries, which keeps it in place. The wind can fan the fire and make its flames rise. When adding fuel to fire it will lead to an explosion. Even the hottest water when poured on fire will still extinguish its flame, and so will a bucket of solid earth.

So far in my twenty-five years of clinical practice I have never come across anyone whose digestion is perfect. Each case is different and sometimes I am surprised how different people can react to the same thing in a totally different way. For example, there is plenty of evidence of the benefits of having a 'green drink or smoothie' in the morning. I will discuss this in more detail in *Chapter Four – The Power of Transformation*; however, now I would like to share how some of my patients have reacted totally differently to the green drink/smoothie.

What is your Agni like?

Irregular or Cold Agni

A forty-eight-year-old mother of two teenage boys, with a busy work and social schedule, travelled a lot and mostly ate salads on the go; her hunger fluctuated and she hardly had any time to chew her food properly. She enjoyed eating sour and salty foods. She complained about feeling constipated and bloated, and at other times acidic with loose motions. She started the green drink and after the initial trial period of three days she wrote to me saying that she felt very uncomfortable, her signs of indigestion hadn't improved and her digestion has worsened.

The only thing I did at that moment was to ask her to use warm water when preparing the drink instead of room temperature water and that made a magical difference. She loved her drink and her symptoms improved within a short period of time – *no more problems*.

What happened here?

IRREGULAR OR COLD AGNI	
Symptoms	**Causes**
unpredictable peristaltic movement leading to constipation or diarrhoea *abdominal distention* *gas and bloating* *lack of stamina* *food intolerances*	*irregular eating habits* *eating on the go* *excess consumption of raw and cold foods* *refined and processed foods* *carbonated and fizzy drinks*

Her lifestyle very much indicated that Vata had gone out of balance. No regular mealtimes and frequent travel increased the 'mobile' quality of Vata. Eating salads intensified the already 'cold' nature of Vata – 'like increases like'. The fact that she was mostly living on salads and not enough sleep demonstrated a lack of feeling grounded, an excess of 'lightness'. All of this contributed to her irregular or cold metabolism. Sometimes her digestion was good, with regular bowel movements. At other times she felt constipated and had all the related symptoms, or she complained about loose bowel motions with symptoms such as acid reflux; all indicators of a cold Agni. She was able to tolerate the green drink better after using warm water because the warm water was soothing to her cold digestion.

Overactive or Heated Agni

Another case involving the same green drink recipe wasa thirty-six-year-old self-employed business manager who confirmed that he felt hungry all the time and couldn't skip meals easily. He needed to have his food at regular times, otherwise he became very grumpy. His main problem was his itchy skin. He loved sour and pungent foods. He started with having a green smoothie/drink in the morning and after the first day reported back to me that he experienced diarrhoea almost immediately after he had the drink, and complained about a burning sensation in his stomach. I asked him to explain to me how he made the drink and exactly what he used. Being Pitta(Pittas often think they know better)and because he liked hot and spicy things, instead of adding a tablespoon of olive oil, he added some red chili oil and almost doubled the amount of fresh ginger mentioned in the recipe, thinking that more was better.

Because he had a more hyperactive metabolism, meaning his digestion was already overheated, by adding more of the ginger plus the chili oil, the heat increased; it was like putting fuel on a fire, which increased his Pitta. Pitta, as stated, is not only made of the element of fire, it also has a water component. In his case, the increased Pitta also had increased the water element, leading to liquid motions. I insisted that he use olive oil and asked him to add some fresh coriander and use the ginger as indicated in the recipe. He followed my directions and was fine. He felt much more energetic and his itchiness decreased after the first week of taking the green drink.

OVERACTIVE OR HEATED AGNI	
Symptoms	**Causes**
burning sensation in stomach	*excess release of acid and enzymes*
excess hunger	*hot and spicy foods*
diarrhoea	*alcohol*
bad breath	*coffee*
cramps when overly hungry	*excess gluten*
headaches when not eating on time	*eating too much*
undigested foods	*medications*
can lead to ulcers, hyperacidity	*psychological and emotional stress*

Underactive or Damp Agni

Constant fatigue, struggles with excess weight, no appetite and excess water accumulation, especially around the ankles, were the main symptoms of a fifty-two-year-old, female office worker. She admitted to having a sweet tooth and that her lifestyle was very sedentary with hardly any exercise, sitting all day in front of the computer. She forgot to eat and sometimes remembered late in the afternoon that she hadn't had any food. So she would grab a sandwich and a muffin on the go. She went home late, and by the time she consumed her dinner it would be around 8pm.In the evenings she would start to crave for sugary things, and that often couldn't be controlled. After starting the green smoothie routine, she called me saying that she had to stop because she felt nauseous after the drink. In her case I altered the recipe slightly, asking her to increase the amount of ginger, to add some watercress and make the drink more liquid.

She had a slow, sluggish and damp hypoactive metabolism. If you have this type of metabolism, the least amount of food will take the longest time to digest. To relieve her symptoms of nausea, all that was needed was to increase the fire by adding some more fresh ginger, watercress because of its pungency, and finally, I suggested to her to make the drink with more water. This made the drink more suitable for her slow digestion. In her case, because her digestion was very slow, having a drink that was more solid was like pouring earth on the fire; it extinguished the flame causing the nausea.

UNDERACTIVE OR DAMP AGNI	
Symptoms	**Causes**
weight gain	*lack of exercise*
high cholesterol	*excess heavy and oily foods such as cheese, deep-fried foods*
lethargy	
fluid retention	*refined foods such as white bread, wheat pasta*
feeling sluggish	
little or no hunger but cravings	*uncontrolled blood sugar levels*
eating late at night	*excess gluten intake*
eating too much	*skipping meals*

Agni transforms food into heightened awareness.

The easiest way, or at least a good starting point, to balance your Agni would be to avoid the causative factors as listed in the tables above. A balanced digestion is when one feels light, physically energetic and mentally clear and alert after a meal. One should neither feel too hungry nor too full after a meal and there should be no symptoms of indigestion such as gas or bloating, acidity or any other discomfort. This is the ideal metabolism where the food takes between three to six hours to be processed.

It has almost become a nightmare for anyone hosting a dinner party because almost every guest will have a different diet. *I can't have any gluten… I can have gluten but no diary… in principle I am vegetarian but eat fish…* and the list can go on and on. My question to you is, if you have a food allergy or intolerance, do you think avoiding the triggering foods is the best solution to the problem? My take on this is, yes. If you know that you have some food intolerance then perhaps for a certain amount of time it is best to avoid those foods. Whilst my clients do this, I work alongside them to strengthen their digestion and make corrections to an impaired metabolism so that foods, when slowly being introduced back again, can be tolerated without adverse symptoms. To me this sounds like a much more 'healthy' plan than trying to refrain from certain foods for the rest of your life and thereby giving up living.

Ayurveda has very effective and simple methods to improve your digestion, which will be discussed in *Chapter Four–The Power of Transformation.* There is no harm in aiming at optimising anyone's digestion, irrespective of whether you are looking for alternative solutions to treating a more serious illness or if it is simply because you aim at health maintenance and wellbeing. The Ayurvedic approach is excellent and can also be used alongside any conventional or other alternative treatment.

Call to Action

Reflecting on the above section, what do you think your digestion is like? If you so wish, there is also a questionnaire at the end of the book that might help you to understand if you are more inclined towards an irregular, overheated or slow metabolism.

Key Concept 6: Tissue Nourishment

*The way you feel today is because of what you have eaten
about forty days ago.*

Ayurvedically, forty days is how long it takes from the initial stages of digestion in your mouth to the time when food is broken down by the hydrochloric acid in the stomach then separated into what is no longer needed (which is excreted as waste) and into the nutrients that provide nourishment to your bodily tissues, and finally into a vital substance called 'ojas'.

Ojas is responsible for holding your entire organism together and for maintaining its functioning. All of this is governed and directed not only by your main gastric fire in the stomach, as discussed in the previous section, but also by your tissue metabolism– the body's ability to absorb and distribute the nutrients that circulate in the blood stream and provide the fuel to build the various tissues.

THE SEVEN DHATUS – BODILY TISSUES			
Dhatu	**Tissue**	**Related Diseases**	**Subtle Meaning**
Rasa	lymph	lymph congestion, thyroid problems, weak immunity	nourishment
Rakta	blood	skin problems, liver conditions, high blood pressure	life
Mamsa	muscle		strength
Meda	adipose	metabolic disorders such as obesity, diabetes	love
Asthi	bones	osteoporosis, hair loss	support
Majja	central nervous system	insomnia, migraines	protection
Shukra	reproductive system	infertility, menstrual disorder	renewal

Each tissue consists of innumerable cells and is being nourished through specific channels through which it receives energy, nutrients and eliminates waste. Health and wellbeing is jeopardised when this nutrient supply is compromised and accumulated waste can't be excreted, which consequently leads to an obstruction of the channels, cutting off the fuel that feeds the engine of the cells of a specific tissue or organ.

In ancient times, before the luxury of modern technology such as x-ray machines, health experts learned to understand human physiology through observation of nature. Whatever has been learned through nature has never proven to be wrong; we just use different terminology today. In fact, many of the surgical instruments still used today are based on design concepts that were first used by Sushruta, one of the exponents of Ayurveda, thousands of years ago.

The seven tissues are nourished in different ways—one way being one tissue feeds the next in a sequential manner. So let's understand this process by looking at nature.

When you churn full fat, good quality milk for an extended period of time, the fat starts to separate on the surface. If you keep churning, this fat turns into cream, which then can be changed into butter from which you can prepare ghee.

The formation of the first tissue, Rasa-lymph, is like the formation of milk. From there on the process of qualitative transformation continues. Lymph is denser and from there the subsequent tissues become more and more subtle. This qualitative transformation becomes more and more complex and complicated. The further the tissues are affected down the line, the more time and effort is needed to correct. For example, asthma, a disease linked to the first tissue, Rasa, can be more easily addressed than osteoporosis, a disease linked to the fifth tissue, Asthi.

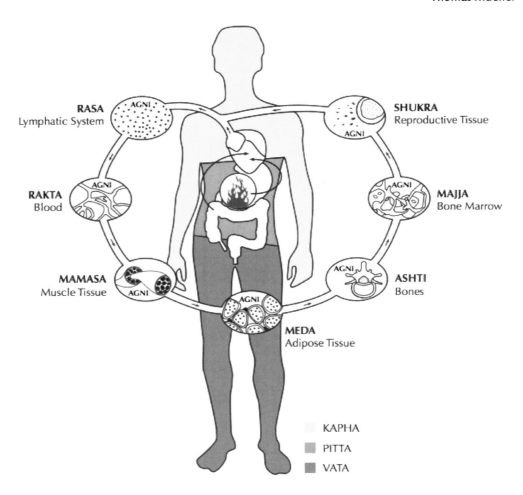

Let me share with you one of my clinical cases to explain the knock-on effect an impaired tissue metabolism can have. A twenty-seven-year-old female, diagnosed with endometriosis, a disease characterised by severe pain, excess bleeding and irregular menstruation, often accompanied by infertility came to see me initially because she had been trying very hard for a couple of years to conceive. During the consultation I assessed her constitution as being Vata-Kapha. Ayurvedically, the second and seventh Dhatu-blood and reproductive tissue respectively were impaired.

The first step I took was to concentrate on the second tissue by correcting her general metabolic fire, which cleared some of the accumulated toxic waste so that the second tissue could receive proper nourishment again. After a couple of months of treatment, her menstruation became regular and her menstrual symptoms slowly reduced. I can share with great joy that at the time I wrote these lines, I received a text message from her with the news that she was carrying a baby boy.

In summary, if one tissue is weak all subsequent tissues will suffer eventually; it is just a matter of time. In her case it affected immediately the reproductive tissue further down the line, because this was her vulnerable spot for any disease to manifest.

Another element which can be overlooked easily during an Ayurvedic assessment is the relationship between the affected tissue and its subtler meaning.

One of my clients, a fifty-eight-year-old artist, struggled with weight issues for many years. It slowly got worse during menopause. This can easily be explained because during menopause the thyroid slows down and produces less oestrogen. Lower levels of oestrogen had slowed down her metabolism. However, there is another dimension to this. Being overweight is linked to impairment in the adipose tissue and the central theme around this fourth tissue is 'love' and 'self-love'.

Besides getting started on the Ayurvedic journey by adjusting her natural rhythms and improving her digestion, I asked her to do a self-massage with warm sesame oil, slowly and with full attention in the morning before her shower.

This was one of the most challenging suggestions anybody had ever made to her. She found it difficult to accept herself, and self-touch with warm oil sounded initially impossible. During the weeks of her treatment it got easier for her. I added another challenge by asking her to do the massage in front of a mirror and when performing each stroke I asked her to repeat the mantra "I love and accept myself the way I am". Without even changing her nutritional regime too much, she slowly but steadily started to drop weight as she was able to 'love' herself again the way she was. Like any holistic practitioner, I think strongly that belief systems affect our wellbeing and the subtler meaning of the affected tissue gives me a clue as to what lies underneath.

The Importance of Ojas

Ojas, as mentioned earlier, is the vital nectar of life that is extracted from food. This vital substance is very much the connecting link between the overall physical structure and our subtler bodies. Because of its refined nature and subtle physical structure it has not yet really been described by modern science. However, it can be recognised and measured because of its overall effects such as immunity, good digestion, radiant skin, general feeling of happiness, purpose and direction in life. Pulse analysis is a good means to measure the quality and presence of this vital substance called Ojas, which protects life.

OJAS – VITAL SUBSTANCE	
When Balanced	**When Imbalanced**
radiant complexion	*chronic illness*
good immunity	*depression*
high threshold for stress	*compromised immunity*
mental clarity	*delicate digestion*
enthusiasm for life	*weak and lack of energy*
energy	*emaciation*
creativity	*feeling sluggish and fatigued*
happiness and contentment	*anxious*

Over the past ten to fifteen years I have seen many clients with a variety of imbalances and diseases, some that are addressed easily such as indigestion or headaches, and others that are more complicated, for example, infertility, chronic illnesses or cancer. According to my observation concerning increasing stress, in a more and more fast-paced society where daily living is driven by speed, most of my clients share common symptoms such as tired and dull looking skin, lack of energy and sluggishness. They are great 'worriers' and many have lost their passion for life.

Here are some of the aspects that compromise that quality and the formation of Ojas:

- low water intake
- lack of exercise
- irregular meal times
- insufficient sleep
- mental and physical stress
- metal toxicity, especially mercury
- acidic foods
- food colourings and preservatives
- smoking and alcohol

One of my main goals when designing a treatment plan is to improve tissue metabolism, which is the basis for healthy formation of the tissues and excellent quality of Ojas. It is my promise to you that when you make use of some of the self-help tools described and suggested in this book, you will improve the quality of your Ojas.

Call to Action

When reflecting on your own health, think for a moment which of your bodily tissues could be weak or affected. Then look at the above table explaining the seven tissues to find out its corresponding subtle meaning. How would you relate the subtle meaning of the affected tissue to your current circumstances, be it health, relationships or other aspects of your personal life? For example, if your immunity is weak, which is related to the first tissue and its subtle meaning is nourishment, ask yourself,

"Do I allow myself to be nourished?"

"What can I do to nourish myself?"

Key Concept 7: Empty the Dustbin

So much attention is paid to what goes into the body, but how much attention do you pay to what comes out of your system? According to Ayurveda this is of equal importance.

When your Agni becomes impaired because of an elemental imbalance, your metabolism is affected. The food you eat could be as healthy as possible, prepared by following all the suggested Ayurvedic principles. But in the case of a retarded Agni, nutrients can't be absorbed and food components remain undigested. These start accumulating in the various tissues and organs and become what is called 'Ama' in Ayurveda. Ama is sticky and clogs the intestines and other channels, such as blood vessels and capillaries. Ama eventually will turn into toxins, which are then absorbed into the blood where they enter general circulation. Ama does not just accumulate because of a weakened digestion; bacterial toxins and emotional disturbances can lead to the formation of Ama also, and when attached to the cellular wall of the weaker tissues in the body, can lead to contraction, clogging, stagnation and weakness of the organs.

There are many ways to find out if your 'dust bin' is full. For example, if your tongue is coated, depending on which part of the tongue is affected, an Ayurvedic practitioner is able to assess where in the body Ama exists.

Ama is not an enemy, rather a natural bodily response.

The problem is when your 'waste disposal system' breaks down. In other words, disease begins when the body fails to clear this toxic waste material. The lymph system is an important part of your bodies 'clean up team'. It aids the immune system in removing and destroying waste, debris, dead blood cells, toxins and even cancer cells. The lymph vessels convey excess fluid containing toxic waste, collected from all over the body, back into the blood circulation. From there it is then eliminated through your sweat glands, the kidneys or your colon.

How often do you empty your 'dust bin?'

There are many ways to prevent the formation of Ama and if it has formed, to eliminate it. For example, exercise stimulates your metabolism and clears the body from unwanted and undigested waste. This is why when you exercise, especially in the morning, you feel more energetic throughout the day as it helps to clear lymphatic congestion. In *Chapter Four* you will find many practical tips as to how to avoid the formation of Ama and how to get rid of it.

The aspect in Ayurveda that is specifically dedicated to detoxification is called 'Panchakarma'. In the next chapter I will explain in great detail how Panchakarma not only gets rid of water soluble toxins but also those that only dissolve in oils or fats which stick to the exterior walls of the tissues, preventing the cells form communicating with each other. These oil soluble toxins are harder to get rid of. They hide the Matrix from sight, but when removed, increase your self-awareness and provide you free access to your own inner healing mechanism.

Call to Action

Have a look in the mirror and check your tongue to see if there is any sign of coating, especially in the morning upon waking. What is the colour of the coating? If it is white then your toxins are mostly because of an imbalance in Kapha. If yellowish in colour then this is probably due to an impaired Pitta, and if darker it is due to Vata.

Key Concept 8: The Six Stages of a Disease Process

Your 'true nature' at the time of birth will give you an indication of your susceptibility towards a certain disease. In other words, your constitution will give away the area that is very likely to be affected first should you lose touch with your individual or higher self.

For example, if your main constitution is Vata then you are more susceptible towards gas and bloating, lower back pain, arthritis, sciatica, insomnia or perhaps neuralgia. Any Vata disease has its origin in the large intestine. The likelihood of a Pitta person to develop gallbladder, bile and liver disorders, hyperacidity, peptic ulcer, gastric or an inflammatory disease is much higher than in a Vata person. A Pitta type could also suffer from skin disorders such as rashes or eczema. In any case a Pitta disease will start in the small intestine. For Kapha, the disease process starts in the stomach and could lead towards tonsillitis, sinusitis, bronchitis and congestion in the lungs.

Taking into consideration all of the above and based on my clinical experience, when a disease starts to show symptoms on a physical level, for example in the stomach, small intestine or perhaps in the colon, then its true origin is in one of the four subtler bodies such as the mental, emotional, energetic or awareness body. I will talk about these different bodies in *Chapter Three– Your Ayurvedic Journey to Wellbeing.*

The moment we lose the connection to our individual or higher self is where we sow the seed of a disease. This is how anger when unaddressed over time, for example, could manifest as an ulcer. Or the emotion of fear as interrupted sleep. Or possessiveness as depression.

But before we get to the manifestation of a disease, any of the three bio-energies must have first accumulated then were further aggravated in their respective homes such as the stomach, small intestine or large intestine, which is the case during Stage One and Two of the disease process. In Stage Three they expand further and move out of their homes where, for example, they relocate in Stage Four somewhere else, until a disease can then be diagnosed in Stage Five with complications arising in Stage Six.

The table below is an example of how the bio-energy of Vata (space and air), when out of balance and not addressed, could manifest in a possible disease.

Stages in Disease Process		Disturbance of Air and Space
1	Accumulation	in the large intestine, making you feel uncomfortable
2	Aggravation	agitation in large intestine, making you feel bloated, fatigued
3	Overflow	spreads through body e.g. lower back pain, stiff joints
4	Relocation	settles in a vulnerable area e.g. lungs

5	Manifestation	diagnosed as asthma
6	Complication	possible respiratory failure

As discussed earlier, health and wellbeing encompasses a harmonious interaction between all the five elements of nature: space, air, fire, water and earth. There are six stages of a disease process. Initially the symptoms are very mild, but you will be aware from Stage One onwards that something is not quite right. The symptoms gradually worsen and a chronic condition usually reflects being in Stage Five, as well as an imbalance in all these five elements, not just one or two. Therefore the healing process should lead towards reversal of the disease process and must involve recognition, as well as the repairing, of these elemental imbalances.

Clinical Examples:

1. Female in her mid-thirties, mother of three children, self-sacrificing for the wellbeing of her children and husband. Typically skips meals, dehydrated, addicted to stimulants to keep her going, excessive or no exercise and lack of rhythm and routine. This indicates a lurking imbalance at Stage Three, moving to four out of six stages of the disease process. It shows primarily as an imbalance in the elements of space, air and earth. Loss of connectedness to herself (element of space), lack of nourishment (earth element) and stability with little to no routine (air element).

2. Male, forty-five years old, overweight, stressed, working long hours, lack of sleep and low energy, leading to comfort eating, irregular meal times, eating late and no energy to exercise. From an Ayurvedic perspective this places him at Stage Four and moving to Stage Five in the disease process. It shows primarily as an imbalance of the elements of air, fire and earth. Extreme stress disrupts the air element. His eating habits have led to the slowing down of the fire element, thus producing an accumulation of toxic waste, which in turn causes weight gain and adversely affects the earth element.

3. Postmenopausal sixty-two-year-old female with chronic insomnia, constipation and osteoporosis. She constantly changes her practitioner to

look for new solutions to her condition. This demonstrates an example of Stage Five of the six stages of a disease process. Most of her symptoms are an indication of severe disruption of the air element. Over many years, due to her lifestyle and nutritional habits, her metabolism has slowed down (element of fire), toxins started to accumulate (element of earth), and as a consequence her body started to dry out (water element) and structural changes took place (element of earth). Her inability to stick to one approach, her impatience to follow things through and her way of giving full responsibility to everyone else but herself indicates that she lacks self-connectedness and trust in the process, which is an imbalanced space element.

The above three examples demonstrate the spectrum of the Ayurvedic stages of the disease process that, if unaddressed over a period of time, naturally progress to further disrupt all the elements. However, it is still possible to at least stop, if not reverse, the degenerative and disintegrative process with the help of Panchakarma, which will be explained in the following chapter.

It is important to take action right from the beginning of the process. Ayurveda, through the technique of pulse analysis, is able to detect any imbalance already in its early stages, unlike conventional medicine. By implementing balancing measures as discussed in *Chapter Four,* Ayurveda is then able to prevent the imbalance from manifesting into a more serious disease.

Prevention is better than cure.

Call to Action

Looking at the example given above and taking into consideration your current understanding of the six stages of a disease process, where do you think you are at?

Key Concept 9: The Need to Find a Natural Rhythm

This section is the last one in this chapter, but the most crucial when trying to understand how Ayurveda is able to restore health and wellbeing. Interestingly when asking students in my workshops and seminars what comes to mind first when thinking about 'living a life in accord with the rhythms of nature' – most of them think about indigenous people on a far remote Island.

A couple of years ago, when travelling to Sri Lanka, hopping from one island to the other, this is exactly what I experienced. No electricity, all life came to a halt as soon as the sun set and daylight faded. Initially this was a very uncomfortable experience for me, being used to unlimited access to electricity and computer work in the evenings. All this was stripped away from me. Instead I was forced

> *"Wellbeing is identifying the natural rhythms within and around us and aligning one's lifestyle as closely as possible with the rhythmic patterns of nature."*
>
> Dr Vijay Murthy

to go to bed naturally, around 8.30 pm or 9 pm at night. At the same time I was so surprised how easy it was for me to get up at 4.30 am just to take in the symphony of nature, listening to the birds sharing their unique musical composition with each other in gratitude of a new day dawning. I could feel each cell of my body taking in the oxygen of the freshest and cleanest air, whilst the first rays of the sun touched my face like a stroke of a loved one saying, "Everything is perfectly alright as it is".

I felt whole and complete and at the time I wondered how we could have lost this connection to the most powerful healer– Mother Nature. It felt so simple and natural at the time to connect to that doctor within again.

Please don't get me wrong. I am not against the developments and advancements of the electronic age but, in a fast paced world like today, in a society where speed has become the driving force of life, there is no greater need for everyone than aligning one's lifestyle with the cycles and rhythms of nature.

Speaking from my own experience, this has been the most challenging aspect on my personal journey. For a substantial period of my life, I lived in a spiritual community where all my physical needs were taken care of. Food was prepared and served three times a day at a specific time, my sleeping and waking cycles were perfectly Ayurvedic, as was the rest of my daily routine with long hours of yoga and meditation practice in the early hours of the morning and late afternoon and some teaching and administration duties in between.

But the challenge for me was when I left that secure and protected environment after ten years. That was when the true test started. How true would I be to my own principles? I can tell you that for many years, and to some extent still today, it was like walking on a wobbly bridge; I could tip over any moment and lose myself in the whirlpool of day-to-day life.

Vata Society

The pace of the current time reflects an excess of the elements of air and space. This has given birth to the 'Vata society', where fast food and lunch on the run is considered fashionable and jet-setting is something to which one should aspire; where grabbing a remote or surfing through the net has become an acceptable means of relaxation and where sleep is considered a waste of time.

Did you know that approximately 70% of all diseases are due to an imbalance of Vata? If you recollect, Vata is made up of the elements of space and air. Space is expansive and has no boundaries, and air is subtle, mobile and light. Because air is subtle, when expanding Vata can take control of your life, often without you realising it. Because space has no boundaries, when Vata gets to a certain point it becomes uncontrollable. This is when it becomes dangerous and results in the manifestation of many of our current diseases.

Recent research published by Opinium Research in the UK in October 2012 revealed that although over three quarters of those families who have children living at home still believe mealtimes are an essential part of family life, a quarter of households that have at least one meal together don't spend more than fifteen to twenty minutes around the table. Half of those who have their meals together have their TV on whilst eating. According to this research, families don't seem to take the time to prepare a meal anymore and they rely on pre-made sauces and ready meals. The trend is that there is less and less time spent as a family talking over a meal, and more and more ready-made meals and quick snacks are being consumed in front of a TV.

Interestingly, not only does this indicate that watching TV has become more important than food, but it also shows the need for permanent stimulation. Thirty images per second are being transmitted by a colour TV, adding up to 1800 images per minute. You are being bombarded with 108,000 images per hour whilst watching TV; fast, flickering, subtle, hardly noticeable, all adding to the 'Vata syndrome' of modern-day living. Perhaps for many of you it might be hard to believe but, up to this day, I still have no TV at home. I was given one by my friend recently and it is still sitting in its box behind the sofa waiting to be installed.

In trying to understand the Vata society, it is helpful to look at different cultures. Each time when traveling to India I ask myself why, despite of all the traffic, noise and permanent external stimulation, do I feel much more calm and relaxed in the middle of chaos in India in comparison with how I feel when walking down Oxford Street in London? What is it? Shouldn't this experience be worse in India than in the West? I am aware that my experience of India most likely does not match the experience of others who have travelled to that side of the globe. However, upon reflection I have come to the conclusion that people in India have a much more balanced life. Despite all the poverty and hectic noise and dust, in general people are happier. They still have a great sense of community; they talk to each other on the streets and visit each other in their homes. Somehow this must have an indirect influence on the way I feel when visiting.

The way you think and feel is influenced by the collective awareness of your surroundings.

Having accepted invitations to many family events such as weddings, sixtieth birthday celebrations, inauguration of buildings and so on, what is common amongst all the families is that people in India know how to celebrate life. They enjoy coming together and preparing food and still value sitting down when having their meal. True friendship, fun and laughter are the necessary elements that keep the active Vata under control; they are the safety net that catches the Vata when balance is lost. …Here am I living for two years in an apartment complex where I don't even know my immediate neighbours.

Vata can react on a subtle, emotional level in two ways: in an extroverted person it can lead to an emotional outburst, a hyperactive mind; for someone who is more introverted it can manifest in the form of depression. In addition, if there is the presence of the element of fire, this can lead to a massive explosion… Watch out when the wind blows into the fire.

Sooner or later a lack of rhythm in life–be it through irregular sleeping and/or eating patterns, loss of direction or the inability to connect to your true nature– will lead to an aggravated Vata with the wind drying out the earth, initially causing symptoms such as excess thirst, lack of sleep, indigestion or tension headaches. This lack of grounding or depleted Kapha further aggravates Vata, leading to bad eating habits, lack of appetite or perhaps pushes you to exercise like crazy, thinking that it will bring you the relaxation needed to recover from the stresses and strains of day-to-day living. Instead, exercising in that state becomes like marching for miles and miles in the scorching desert heat, chasing a water hole that does not exist. You have lost your balance and are caught in a vicious circle that has to be broken.

Another interesting aspect to mention is that the space element in Vata is the Matrix, which provides access to the subtler bodies, including the awareness body. It builds the bridge to your subconscious and psyche and when tapped into will bring you in touch with your 'doctor within'. When the air element in Vata takes over, due to lack of rhythm for example, you start chasing the water oasis in the desert, making you enrol in a new class straight away, inspiring you to try a new practitioner every couple of weeks or to change your diet like your socks. You are desperately looking for solutions anywhere outside of yourself without realising that the very solution has never left you and has always been with you. When you lose access to the element of space, the disease process starts.

Ask yourself the question: "Do I live life or is life living me?"

In *Chapter Four* you will find many useful self-help tools that, when incorporated in your daily life, help you to align your lifestyle as closely as possible with the rhythms of nature. This is no doubt the first step and the pre-requisite for improved wellbeing and better health.

Call to Action

Find a quiet space and draw a table with two columns. In the first column write down all the things you do on a daily basis that affect your Vata such as eating cold foods, staying up late at night, surfing the net, working on the computer or watching TV. In the second column estimate how much time you spend on each of these activities. Add up the time and introduce a daily practice of at least thirty minutes that helps you to get in touch again with the rhythm of nature. This could be a yoga or mediation practice, walking in nature, listening to relaxing music, reading an inspirational book instead of watching TV or getting the paint brush out to express your creativity. surprised how much thirty minutes of rhythm re-alignment practice helps you to feel grounded and calms an aggravated Vata.

....the pressure became so intense that somehow, at some point during my forced resting period, I must have surrendered to whatever was going on around me. I was too exhausted. The aggravating lifestyle and lack of rhythm from weeks of travel had finally caught up with me. As my mental agitation started to calm down, so did the chatter of my mind and with that my tension headaches reduced. One morning during the first few days of my stay at the Vedic centre, I woke up and to my surprise realised that the physical and emotional disharmony had gone. It felt as if it had been washed away by the heavy rainfall of that night. I was well into teaching my Ayurveda course when I started to notice that although I could not understand or speak any Japanese, I could pick up when my translator, whilst eagerly moving the pages of her dictionary in an uncertain and tremulous voice, conveyed the knowledge and principles discussed in my lecture in a slightly distorted manner.

With no more than three to four hours of sleep I felt more energetic and mentally refreshed than having slept for eight or ten hours. I was able to move through each day with ease and such a sense of peace, like a white swan gliding across the silent waters of a holy lake. Listening to the song of silence finally had become the Matrix leading me to an incredible source of energy and peace, to a place where we all speak the same language, a part of me that remained hidden from my awareness because of my resistance to listen to the silence and my need to control my life.

$P = p - i$

My experience in the Vedic centre is encapsulated in Timothy Gallwey's book *The Inner Game,* I n which he says that **P** (performance) can either be enhanced by growing **p** (potential) **or** by decreasing **i** (interference).

In an environment where there is least interference your resistance towards change drops naturally, bringing you increased performance at the same time your potential grows. In a Vastu home, symmetry creates harmony with the least resistance and this becomes your Matrix that allows you to enter that heighted state of awareness I talked about in my first chapter–the state of increased potential which again enhances your performance. So in this case we have growing potential **and** least interference, potentising your performance. The new formula would be **Vastu: $P^2 = p - i$**

You may not be in a position to construct your 'ideal home', but another reason that I shared the story above with you is that your home is your body, which needs looking after. You could have the best central heating system in your home, but if there is air in the pipes, it won't heat up the rooms. Similarly, if your internal system is blocked, your tissues won't get the nutrients needed to keep you going. It is not enough looking after one room; it is each individual room that makes up the perfect home. I would like to encourage you to listen to the effect certain elements have on your body, to keep your fire going and your dustbin empty. Each element in your body has a particular function and a state of perfect health is achieved when they work in harmony with each other: "The whole is greater than the sum of its parts." (Aristotle)

In this chapter I have discussed the building blocks that, when placed together with patience and care, will result in the most perfect and functional home you could ever imagined living in; a body that is full of youthfulness where there is no clutter; an abode where energy flows freely, which keeps you warm when needed and cool when desired; a place to celebrate and enjoy life.

What If

- What if you discovered a way to effectively optimise your metabolism so you are able to minimise food intolerances?

- What if you achieved alignment of your individual rhythms with the cycles and rhythms of nature to experience increased energy and wellbeing?

- What if your external environment supports your ability to learn and comprehend with least resistance?

Call to Action

Clutter around you produces clutter within. Internal chaos is a reflection of what goes on in our external environment. Just think, "Do I really need all of this stuff around me?" If you find it difficult to allow change into your life, irrespective of whether on a physical, mental and/or emotional level, take a brave first step and unclutter your living space. This will bring fresh energy into your home. Clutter is dead energy; it just sits there. It holds you back energetically and becomes like a burden you keep carrying on your shoulders. Less is more. Keep a few pieces that might be very precious to you but look after them well. This is the first step to improve your health and increase your wellbeing.

Amrita – Nectar of the Natural Health Matrix:

- True health is restoring the connection of body, mind, senses and soul.

- Don't wait for your system to break down; start taking responsibility today.

- A compromised digestion is the root cause for any disease.

- By finding out your true nature you gain access to the *Natural Health Matrix*.

- Spend time to eat with your family in a quiet and relaxed environment.

- Your health will improve if you reduce your resistance to change.

THREE ~ AIR

Your Ayurvedic Journey To Wellbeing

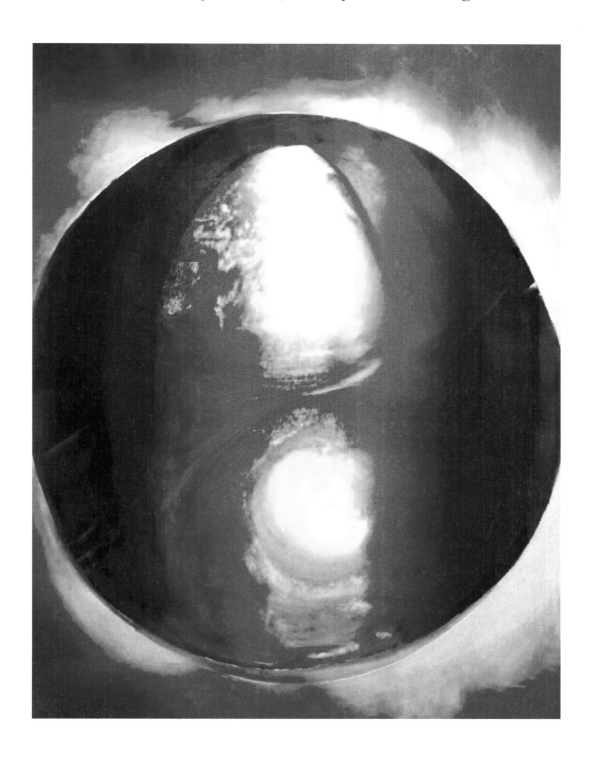

Telephone conversation:

"I am really sorry Thomas, but I can't keep up my promise to be your sponsor so you can make your new life in the country. I did not realise that it is so expensive and there are all these legal requirements, which I can't fulfil..."

"Fantastic, but what am I supposed to do now? I have booked my ticket, my flight is scheduled for Friday, I have closed the chapter 'Europe', reduced my life down to one suitcase and now this..."

"I am so sorry, Thomas..."

There is no way to change my plans now. Somehow something will work out, I just have to jump and trust the process.

I have no idea where to go, where to stay and what to do when I arrive at the other end of the globe. The only things I have with me are a small suitcase and 800.00 Deutschmarks in my pocket.

"Gidday mate... Welcome to Australia; where are you heading?"

"I am just on my way to New Zealand, stopping over at the Sunshine Coast for a couple of days to visit someone I met recently."

"May I see your return ticket from New Zealand?"

"Oh, return ticket? I don't have a return ticket. I wasn't aware that I actually need one."

"Yes, you do Mr Mueller. I am sorry but without a return ticket we can't let you travel to New Zealand. Don't worry; you have got a couple of days to organise a ticket before your scheduled flight to New Zealand."

I can't believe this. Now I have to use the money that was planned to tide me over for the first couple of weeks in New Zealand to buy a ticket. Great. I wonder what's next. No contact in New Zealand, no one and no place to stay. But a return ticket ... how useful is that going to be?

I don't know. I should have really thought first before acting and used my brain and not followed my heart. I guess my family is right when they say that I am crazy leaving Europe and thinking that I can make it on a remote island such as New Zealand in the Pacific Ocean on the opposite side of the world. It could not be any further away from home. I must have lost touch with reality. Am I running away from something? How am I going to survive? I don't even know anyone. Who is going to pick me up once I arrive in Auckland? Where do I go from there? Millions of questions, lots of fears and no answers. Deep within me, however, I know it is the right thing to do and I just have to keep going. No way back; I have come too far...

In This Chapter We Discuss:

- The three phases of wellbeing
- A six step process towards total rejuvenation
- The five bodies and their importance on your Ayurvedic journey.

Why is This Chapter Called 'Air'?

Continuity is an essential aspect of life. This chapter is based on the element air. Air being the force that brings about change through continuous expansion within the 'space' and the building blocks of 'earth' that form the basis of the previous chapters. Although we often use the terms 'beginning' and 'end' to refer to the processes of life, health and the journey through illness or recovery, these points of reference only serve to remind us of those events. However, in reality all beginning and end points, along with all that happens in between, are simply continuous events of movement. This innate aspect of movement is what characterises the element air. If you could imagine walking through a museum with revolving doors, long corridors and huge rooms with displays of art, in a similar way we use our mind, body, emotions and spirit to travel through the passages of health, illness and wellbeing within the boundaries of time and space.

In this chapter I will take you through those doors and passages that will lead you to complete health and wellbeing. As with the example of a museum, no matter which door you take, where you start, where you stop or in which room you spend more time, all of these lead to a rich experience. However, if you had the privilege to be guided by an experienced curator or art historian, the richness of your experience would become far more effective within a short period of time. On the other hand, if you had to figure out the layout of the museum, the maps, the history, all by yourself without any guidance, no doubt you would be enriched through the power of self-exploration, but you may need to spend far more time and energy to reach the same goal. This chapter can be the guide that can make your journey rich and meaningful without the expense of spending too much time exploring.

The Process of the Ayurvedic Journey: 3 Steps to Wellbeing

After having laid the foundation regarding the philosophical basis of Ayurveda and after discussing its building blocks, this chapter looks at the process of the Ayurvedic journey. You cannot reach the goal without understanding the process. The Ayurvedic journey is a journey of discovery where the starting point for each person is very likely to be different. You may face certain challenges; you may wish to take detours along the way or choose to get 'off the train' and have a stop at a particular place. But it is always helpful to come back to the three key landmarks along the path. In order to achieve the desired state of wellbeing, I will also discuss six specific methods as to how to get to those landmarks.

The Ayurvedic journey is a journey of discovery.

In this chapter I also share with you how, through my clinical practice, I have observed that besides the influence of a Vata, Pitta or Kapha personality, everyone experiences life primarily through one of the five bodies. These five bodies are:

- the physical body or earth body
- the energetic body linked to the element of fire
- the mental body related to air
- the emotional or water body
- the awareness body or space body.

In order to design an effective treatment programme for my clients, I need to assess which of the five bodies is more active. This determines the treatment approach I need to take. I will go into greater detail in explaining the five bodies as the chapter unfolds.

If you embark on the Ayurvedic journey, you will certainly not know at the beginning what will cross your path or what challenges will come along your way. But if you stay with the process and keep the final goal in mind, the outcome of improved health and wellbeing will follow.

> "The spiritual journey is individual, highly personal. It can't be organised or regulated. It isn't true that everyone should follow one path. Listen to your own truth."
>
> Ram Dass

No matter where you start on your personal journey or how far away you are from this path to wellbeing, in summary there are three landmarks:

Step 1:   Reconnect with or awaken your inner self-healing ability.

Step 2:   Promote repair and rejuvenation through Panchakarma, a deep cleansing programme.

Step 3:   Maintain the newly found state of health and wellbeing.

In order to understand the process, let me use a metaphor. Imagine you have just inherited from your aunt an antique painting by a famous artist, and when you are in possession of the artwork, you discover that it would fit perfectly in your living room. But to your disappointment, the colours of the painting have faded, some part of the artwork has been damaged and the frame needs changing to match the style of your living room.

Depending on your personality, you would take a slightly different approach to start the process of restoring the painting. If you are more in touch with your 'water or emotional body', you may take the picture with you into your bedroom and, in a reflective mode, remember your aunt and all the nice experiences you had with her. You may try to connect to her emotionally and feel her energy.

On the other hand, if your 'space or awareness body' is most active, your inquisitive nature and perhaps a more analytical mind inspires you to go straight to Google to find out all the details about the artist and the value of the painting. If you experience your life mainly through your 'air or mental body', your first action might be to go immediately to the kitchen, grab a cloth and some cleaning liquid and eagerly start wiping the dust off the painting, which I very much hope you would not do.

In any case, if your mind is cluttered and if you are feeling overwhelmed, you might make the wrong decision over the painting. The most sensible way to decide is just to 'let the ripples of the water settle', and after some reflection time and exploring all your options, you can make an informed decision as to how to deal with the situation.

STEP 1
Reconnect With or Awaken Your Inner Self-Healing Ability

In order to get to the first landmark on your journey towards improved health and wellbeing, where you reconnect with or awaken your inner self-healing ability, you must give yourself permission to rest. A deep state of rest experienced by one's body and mind is absolutely essential before any repair or rejuvenation can occur. The most obvious way in which the body does this is through sleep. Any disturbance in the quality of sleep is a critical indicator of one's body or mind struggling to stay well.

For instance, inability to rest, difficulty in falling asleep, struggling to experience deep sleep or even worse waking up frequently whilst attempting to sleep during the night, are common indicators of extreme stress. An article published in 2004 in *Nature Reviews Immunology* reports that if you get up around three o'clock in the morning, this will weaken your immune system immediately, making you vulnerable to viral and other infections within the next twenty-four hours. Also, several International studies report consistent increased risk for obesity amongst people suffering from poor quality of sleep. Although we assume that sleep is a natural phenomenon, you might be surprised to know that being able to rest is a skill that one needs to develop for long-term health and wellbeing.

The purpose of this chapter is not to teach you how to improve your quality of sleep. However, the techniques described in *Chapter Four* will enable you to develop the skill of deep rest that will result automatically in experiencing deep sleep.

At this point of your journey, I wish to mention that there is a two-step process for achieving a state of deep rest and relaxation.

1. **Observe**: First, touch base with your individual self, where your mind is in its most natural state—a state of least resistance. This is easier said than done. How would you recognise that you are in that state? This is where the self-help tools, by influencing the circadian rhythms, will assure you of experiencing that natural state.

2. **Be**: From this neutral state of the mind you tap into a heightened state of awareness, a state of non-conditioning, where repair can occur, where your reconnect with and reawaken your own inner self-healing mechanism. This can be achieved through specific Ayurvedic therapies or mental rest and repair techniques as explained in Chapter Four.

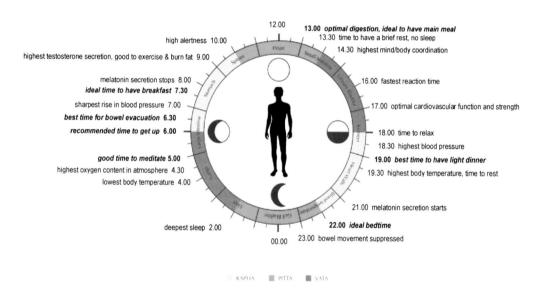

A combination of self-help tools, Ayurvedic therapies and rest and repair techniques, when implemented by aligning your circadian rhythms, will slow down or even stop all unwanted neurological stimulation that interferes with your physiological state.

STEP 2
Promote Repair and Rejuvenation Through a Deep Cleansing Programme

The second landmark on your Ayurvedic journey to wellbeing is to promote repair and rejuvenation by taking you through a step-by-step preparatory phase, leading to an in-depth cleansing programme called Panchakarma.

Panchakarma is the Ayurvedic cleansing process. During the course of a Panchakarma treatment, different methods of cleansing are used depending on your constitution and your health goals. Panchakarma is not a diet or a package that could be described as a three-day or six-week programme, although I wouldn't be surprised to see several online Panchakarma service providers who will provide you a menu of a three-, seven- or twenty-one-day programme. Whilst doing something good for your health is better than doing nothing, sometimes it makes sense that nothing is better than nonsense. As all of us will have travelled a path of health that is unique, it is the task of a good practitioner to adjust and align Panchakarma cleansing to suit a particular need at any given point in time. When Panchakarma is carried out, as will be described in the method section, irrespective of the duration, intensity or types of treatment offered, they all will result in cellular repair and rejuvenation and help in reversing the disease states.

STEP 3
Maintain the Newly Found State of Health and Wellbeing

Doing step one is like having a well-manufactured violin, step two is like tuning the strings perfectly and step three is like performing your favourite tune, which of course is health and happiness. Although your talent in playing violin might always have existed in your being, the absence of a good instrument and untuned strings can only produce a wrong sound. It is also not enough to have a perfect instrument and the talent; the most important thing in determining the success of your performance is practising your talent using your well-maintained instrument. The third step is, in fact, the ultimatum of experiencing health, youth and wellbeing through regular maintenance. In the method section I will explain further the approaches for maintenance of continued health.

After Panchakarma, your body is like a white screen that is able to reflect any image being projected in a most effective manner. At this stage, after you have done the cleansing regime, your cellular metabolism will have improved, your tissues will be strong and healthy and your energy will flow more freely, leading to improved cellular communication. Your body is now naturally able to decode the information contained in any supplement or herb that you may take and to fully allow its biochemical constituents to act most efficiently.

Often you will find after Panchakarma that you are more in touch with what is suitable for you and what is not. Your rhythms are more likely to come back in line with the rhythms of nature; you will then want to maintain your newly found state of wellbeing. Regular Panchakarma is recommended at least once a year, depending on your lifestyle and your individual needs. For example, either to prevent accumulation of toxic waste or to keep improving health, or if you suffer from any chronic illness, Panchakarma can be recommended with every change of season. If you cannot take the time to do a full Panchakarma retreat, at least you can follow a self-care cleansing programme at regular intervals.

The Six Methods to Total Rejuvenation

Coming back to the analogy of the inherited artwork, I don't say that you are a piece of dust like the artwork that needs touching up. You could be the perfect painting or have a good state of health already. But you are still exposed to the elements, so the need to find strategies for health maintenance can be crucial.

Your Health is your most precious bank account.

Perhaps think like this ... Your health is like a bank account. Anything that you invest will multiply and be of use later. Many of my clients who come to seek help have said that they never used to be sick; their immunity had always been strong and it had been only lately that they experienced feeling unwell or developed an illness or disease. In some of these cases I would say that perhaps they were born with a good 'health account', or initially they took great care of themselves. However, over years of exposure to stress and the demands of life, where they believed in the need to push themselves beyond the limits in order to succeed in life, the account has been slowly but steadily reduced until signs and symptoms of illness have manifested and finally they are forced to declare 'bankruptcy'. Health resources have been overspent; the account has been slowly but steadily running empty as no attention has been paid over years to top up the account or to ensure there are enough funds kept in the account.

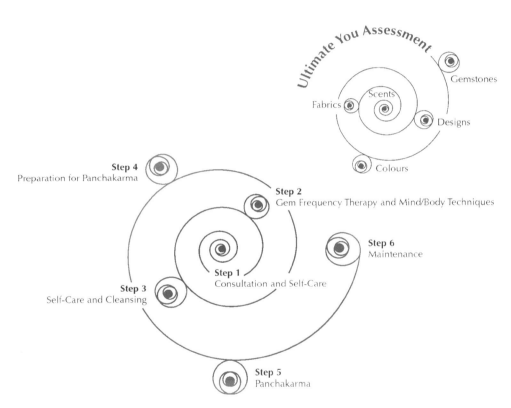

Ayurveda is a lifestyle, not necessarily just a set of practices and medicines, and thus requires a determined commitment towards change from you. It is not a quick fix. It is the openness to understand the complexity of how your physical health is influenced by the subtler bodies, which can unlock the key to better health. Your Ayurvedic journey is a journey of wellbeing and that state of wellbeing provides the platform for rejuvenation. Each journey is different and, as you explore the landmarks/steps and follow the methods discussed in this section, you will naturally acquire a new lifestyle that becomes your second nature. Also, the *Ultimate You Assessment*, which will be discussed in *Chapter Five–The Feel-Good Approach to Wellbeing,* adds to your newly found lifestyle and will enable you to recover and top up your health account. It just takes a fair amount of trust in yourself and the process, and then you will see your health account will never run empty again.

METHOD 1 - Consultation and Introduction to Self-Care

Irrespective of where you start on your Ayurvedic journey, your journey will begin with the initial *Ayuwave* Five Body Assessment and an analysis of your tongue, nails and pulse to determine your nature or your actual constitution and your current state of health.

Of all the traditional diagnostic methods, none is more legendary than pulse diagnosis. It has been used for centuries, not only in Ayurvedic and Chinese medicine, but also in Ancient Rome. The great physician Galen (129–200 AD) was the great master of pulse diagnosis and he wrote a treatise on the subject entitled *De Pulsibus*in which he shared his struggle in mastering the subject:

> *"For many years, I was doubtful about clearly discerning the movement of contraction by touch, and I shelved the question until such time as I could learn enough to fill the gap in my knowledge. After that, the doors of the pulse were open to me."*
>
> Galen. 'De Pulsibus'

During my training in Ayurveda many years ago, we had to practise for months just to feel our own pulse before being allowed to feel someone else's pulse. There are various techniques that are taught today, mostly passed on through oral tradition based on an apprenticeship model as opposed to learning it yourself by reading books. There is no 'one' method. The accuracy of pulse diagnosis is determined by the level of sensitivity, intuition and experience of the reader. As a practitioner, it is essential to allow oneself when reading the pulse to be in a state of 'true self', without any preconceptions, and then listen to what the pulse says.

Think of the pulse as pulsating awareness, a beating heart representing the river of life of the person whose pulse is felt. It tells its own story. The river has its own rhythm, wave and crest. It can flow fast or slow; its water can feel cold or warm. Perhaps there are obstructions in the flow and it might be high or low. Just as a river connects different landmarks and can carry certain objects, blood not only transports nutrients to and from the cells and organs but will carry impressions, memories and energy, making it palpable to the fingers of an experienced practitioner. This is very similar to the experience of identifying notes and the absence of it by an expert musician. With each contraction of the heart, the arteries pulsate, and when touched during pulse diagnosis, the fingertips become receptors that are able to translate the intelligence and information in the pulse into a more concrete image, relating it to the five elements, which then combine in three distinct ways in physical form as the three Doshas of Vata, Pitta and Kapha

> *"The same stream of life that runs through my veins night and day runs through the world and dances in rhythmic measures. It is the same life that shoots in joy through the dust of the earth in numberless blades of grass and breaks into tumultuous waves of leaves and flowers."*
>
> *Rabindranath Tagore*

Based on the assessment of pulse, tongue and nails, the possible underlying cause for any imbalance or ailment is discussed by looking at how the subtler dimensions such as the mental, emotional, awareness and energetic body influence the biochemistry of the physical body. Finally, a treatment plan is discussed that works for you based on the principle that 'less is more', by introducing the basic principles that help you to align your lifestyle as closely as possible with the rhythms of nature. This is no doubt the first step and pre-requisite for improved wellbeing and increased feeling of rejuvenation.

Self-care Methods to Improve Wellbeing and Promote Rejuvenation:

- ○ Realign your rhythm with the rhythm of nature by establishing an ideal morning and evening regime.
- ○ Balance nutrition by following specific Ayurvedic principles and using certain foods and spice mixes to suit your constitution.
- ○ Use Ayurvedic remedies such as food, herbal powders, herbal tablets, herbal tinctures and herbal pastes.

METHOD 2 - Marma and Gem Frequency Therapy, Introduction to Mind-Body Techniques and Other Essential Therapies

During this phase of your Ayurvedic journey, you will be introduced to various Ayurvedic therapies, in particular to the *Ayuwave* Gem Frequency Therapy.

The *Ayuwave* Gem Frequency Therapy is the signature treatment of *Ayuwave* health and wellbeing. It is an essential aspect of its Quantum Healing approach, which understands that the physical body ultimately is a field of information and intelligence, energy in motion. With this in mind, healing occurs when there is a shift in the information field that might have gone out of balance having resulted in ill-health. Quantum Healing uses awareness to change awareness towards an improved state of being.

The *Ayuwave* Gem Frequency Therapy combines Marma Therapy with the timeless knowledge of Ayurvedic Gem Therapy, using the latest state of the art technology. Light resembling full spectrum sunlight is passed through specialised gem-cups containing precious and semi-precious gem stones with the help of 18 carat gold or solid silver pins and colour filters. Low emitted electromagnetic frequencies (alpha, beta, theta or gamma waves), white noise and Schumann resonance are then passed through these gem-cups to further intensify the healing potential of the gemstones, especially by directing the rays to Ayurvedic Marma points on the client, along with the use of specific essential oils. This subtle treatment changes the body's bioenergetics by providing direct access to the Matrix of natural health, the door to self-repair. It produces a straight line to the doctor within and thereby the body's own pharmacy.

There are about 108 Marma points, or vital energy points, along the Ayurvedic meridians of the body. When gently energised through gem light and touched in a particular way, Marma points signal to the body to produce exactly what is needed, including neurochemicals and hormones that initiate the healing process on all the five elemental bodies. Based on the understanding that your body knows best what to do, a state of homeostasis– a process where the body attempts to regain or maintain a state of stable physiological balance– is achieved. For example, if you get too cold, your body will maintain homeostasis by causing shivering, which will warm you up. Or if your glucose levels are too high in the blood, a hormone called insulin is secreted by the pancreas to stimulate the absorption of glucose by the cells. The *Ayuwave* Gem Frequency Therapy helps to regulate internal conditions by triggering a self-feedback control towards improved health and wellbeing.

Therapeutic Grade A essential oils add to the potency of this treatment. Essential oils are like the blood of the plant. Because of their high oxygenating quality, when applied to these junction points and energised with gem light these oils are the connecting link between the physical and non-physical. Increased oxygen supply to the cells encourages tissue repair, a pre-requisite to promote youthfulness and rejuvenation.

"Marma Therapy is extremely relaxing. After my treatment the changes I felt were more energy, connected, inspired and more sense of self. The impact of the treatment was amazing in allowing me to understand and be more aware of myself. Amazing."

Sarah, Acupuncturist

Before I discuss further methods under this section, let me share one of my clinical cases with you where the *Ayuwave* Gem Frequency Therapy has been used as a complementary approach in the treatment of a terminal illness such as cancer.

In November 2013 a young gentleman, age 29 came to see me for a consultation. He had been diagnosed with a rare type of cancer, only generally found in people who are indigenous to the Indian subcontinent. At that time he was given six months based on the rarity of the tumour and its rate of growth. From a medical perspective removal and basically trial and error treatment were the only options because there was no specific medical treatment for this type of cancer. During the course of his treatment at the *Ayuwave* clinic, from November 2013 until March 2014 he had undergone thirteen different types of chemotherapies, interspersed with surgeries, initially every two weeks and at times twice weekly. His state of health was monitored by an oncologist and they kept removing the malignant growth but it kept growing closer and closer to his skull. At some stage during those five months, it was getting pretty close to needing to do bone crafting or replacing a part of his skull with a titanium plate. The trajectory of the tumour itself was directly above his brain and would have caused a fatal stroke had it grown through the skull bone. As soon as we started with the gem frequency therapy in November the rate of growth slowed down drastically and after we stopped during the Christmas break in December, it had grown substantially. When we started again in the middle of January, the growth of the tumour slowed down again and its pattern became more organised and less chaotic. Alongside this, the client was introduced to meditation and specific breathing techniques, he changed his diet and learned how to deal with his emotions. Today (May 2014) this young man is officially in his second month of remission.

"I have never felt more conscious as a human being. I feel the world is my oyster. This is really a turning point in my life and it is probably the best experience I have ever had, which is ironic, as it has been the hardest time in my life needing to deal with this cancer. I now work in the context of the world, as opposed to the world working for me."

Nik, Client

Whilst the *Ayuwave* Gem Frequency Therapy is done by a practitioner, mind-body techniques can be practised on your own. The steps and benefits will all be explained in detail in Chapter Four.

In addition to the above described therapy and other mind-body practices a range of essential Ayurvedic therapies can be very helpful, not only in assisting the effectiveness of the programme but also during the maintenance phase. In other words, these can be done at any stage in your journey. Let's review some of them:

Abhyanga

This is a traditional Ayurvedic whole body therapy involving body massages by incorporating Ayurvedic meridians and Marma points. As skin is the largest organ forming the boundary between the internal and the external, it is responsible for detoxification. Abhyanga keeps the skin healthy, improves circulation, supports lymphatic flow and thereby improves immunity. Traditional Ayurvedic Abhyanga is performed by using specific oils, sometimes herbal oils that suit one's constitution and current health needs. Unlike relaxation or sports massage, Abhyanga, although providing immense relaxation and working remedially, mainly re-organises the individual's bioenergetics pathways, thereby improving tissue repair and bringing about rejuvenation. It can be done on anyone from infancy to old age, including during pregnancy.

Synchronised Abhyanga

Synchronised Abhyanga, wherein two specialised therapists perform massage-like strokes that leave the recipient in a state of heightened relaxation comparable to bliss, is unique to Ayurvedic tradition. The synchronised rhythmical movements and pressure of the massage strokes have a profound effect on the central nervous system by helping to balance the right and left hemisphere of the brain. It thereby creates a state of homeostasis, where the body and mind are encouraged to remember how it is to function normally. This is essential for any healing to occur. Although the basic principles of Synchronised Abhyanga are very similar to Abhyanga, the coordination and the fine skills employed by the therapists make it an extraordinary experience. It has all the benefits of Abhyanga, except it acts faster and the effects last longer.

Padabhyanga

This is an Ayurvedic reflexology treatment that is grounding and relaxing. This therapy changes the biological clock to match the rhythms of nature by focusing on the area between the knees to the feet. It revitalises the entire body and can be useful in the treatment of early signs of depression, insomnia, stress or generally tired feet and legs.

Pristhabhyanga

This Ayurvedic therapy focuses on the lower back, the junction point of major nerves and the so-called second brain. It links the spine with our central nervous system and helps to relieve backache, tensions and strains. It also addresses the psychological aspects of the nervous system.

Kati Basti

A dam made from dough is placed on a specific area of the back, depending on the needs of the client. Warm oil is poured into the dam where it remains to nourish the affected area deeply. Kati Basti acts on the musculoskeletal system and works well with structural changes. It reduces inflammation of the nerves pressing on bones and addresses chronic back pain. A series of sessions are recommended for this treatment to be effective.

Shiroabhyanga

This is a traditional Ayurvedic head treatment based on the thirty-six Marma or reflex points on the head. The head and brain are the controlling centre and the receiving point of the vital force Prana. This therapy acts on the hypothalamus, thus is useful in hormonal conditions, stress and sleep-related disorders. It relaxes and soothes the head, neck and shoulders.

Vishesha

This massage is a special, deep tissue therapy, which removes blockages and stimulates lymphatic flow. It soothes those deeper muscular aches and pains and removes stiffness and sluggishness. Vishesha massage is highly refreshing and energising.

Garshana

The use of silk gloves in this massage creates gentle friction, which helps to increase blood and lymphatic circulation, thereby helping to oxygenate cells and stimulate the removal of accumulated toxins. Garshana also breaks down fat deposits, cleanses and exfoliates the skin and assists the process of normalising weight.

Mukhabhyanga

This Ayurvedic facial treatment is like a natural facelift, using a prescriptive and homemade Ayurvedic skin-care range to treat the Marma points, or energy points, of the head to stimulate circulation and lymphatic flow. A specific technique is used to increase cerebrospinal fluid thus strengthening the nervous system. It also supports normal function of pituitary and pineal glands. This Ayurvedic facial treatment has a toning effect on eyes and inner organs, promoting a healthy complexion and regeneration of a younger looking skin.

Nasya

Administration of specially prepared herbal oils through the nasal passages is the basic function of Nasya. In this treatment the client will go through an elaborate ritual of Ayurvedic face massage, steam inhalation, application of hot towels, followed by administration of herbal oils into the nostrils. In this luxurious and intensely powerful treatment, the sinuses around the nose are cleansed. In Ayurveda, the nose is considered as the gateway to the head, meaning all the imbalances relating to the sinuses, blood vessels, nerves and glands in this region receive the benefit of Nasya. The effect of this treatment is a range of health benefits such as improvement in migraines, premenstrual tension, insomnia, depression, anxiety, eye strain, clarity of mind, as well as the reduction of headaches and the signs of ageing.

Netra Basti

This is a specific treatment comparable to an eye bath, wherein pure clarified organic butter is heated to lukewarm temperature and gently poured into a dam built around the eye socket, which instantaneously gives immense relaxation to the eyes, which is an unusually comfortable experience. It is very useful in eyestrain, to reduce dark circles, to improve circulation in the region of the eyes, to improve headaches and eyesight, to make eyes look brighter and it also helps to improve clarity of the mind.

METHOD 3 - Reinforcement of Self-care and Introduction to Cleansing Programme

During the course of your journey you will build up slowly your self-care first aid kit. It is important that changes are made slowly in order not to feel overwhelmed. Gradually, various practices are being introduced, keeping in mind that sometimes little changes can have a profound effect.

Also, you will be introduced slowly to a gently cleansing regime such as having a liquid day, where you may have green smoothie specifically for your constitution or liquid soups only, such as chicken soup or vegetable broth. The best time to do these cleansing days is on the day of a new moon or on a Saturday.

Fasting supports elimination and detoxification. Although the best day, astrologically, for fasting is on a Sunday, cleansing can be done whenever you have the time to do it. It can be repeated on a monthly basis as often or as long as you can sustain the practice. At some stage during this process, you might even want to progress to a laxative day, using prescribed herbs for a gentle bowel cleanse, followed by specific diet.

METHOD 4 - Preparation for Panchakarma

Method 4is like making sure all the rubbish is gathered together and ready for disposal and Method 5 is the act of emptying the rubbish bin. As you can imagine, cleaning and gathering the rubbish takes longer than emptying. In this way, once you have done a few cleansing days, you will be ready and prepared for the finale of Panchakarma.

As indicated at the beginning of the chapter, this is a journey and the speed with which you embark on the journey is completely up to you. In any case, it is my promise to you that, if you follow the procedures and suggestions discussed in the fourth chapter of this book, you will be well on your way to experiencing improved wellbeing. Generally speaking, you need to allow three to six months of consistent application of your prescribed Ayurvedic self-care programme and rest and repair regime to start gently the healing process in preparation for Panchakarma. Irrespective of which cleansing procedure will be prescribed, in order to maximise the benefit and to reduce any possible adverse reactions, proper preparation is absolutely essential and the process should not be rushed.

The aim of Panchakarma is to soften and bring toxins from the minute channels to the most obvious and largest channel in the body, the digestive tract, which has the capacity for elimination when directed properly. This is a process that takes place in several stages. Firstly, it is essential to reduce additional sources of toxins by following a specific dietary regime and by initiating detoxification through the taking of specific Ayurvedic herbs for three to seven days. This will improve your digestive ability so you will be better able to handle the next stage, which is the consumption of clarified butter, or ghee, specifically prepared according to your constitution and health goals.

Don't be scared by the mention of the word 'ghee' or clarified butter. Thankfully, after three decades of longitudinal studies, we now know that fat does not necessarily make fat, it is the refined carbohydrates combined with fats that has resulted in obesity as a major problem in our society today. We blame the butter whilst the culprit is the bread.

The consumption of medicated ghee is over three to seven days, in gradually increasing dosages. Ideally, this medicated ghee step should be undertaken within a retreat setting, as close monitoring may be required and necessary when taking medicated ghee, especially when being undertaken for the first time. In certain circumstances I allow my clients to undertake this step in their own home setting under close supervision, provided the essential criteria and requirements are taken into consideration. This would include planning in-home visits during this process to assess, supervise and make any necessary adjustments to the process and instructions.

The purpose of taking ghee is to flood the circulation with triglycerides. Ghee, when taken internally, over a maximum period of seven days in increasing dosages, creates a concentration gradient between fats inside the cells and the plasma, which promotes the movements of the toxins from the cells into the gastrointestinal tract. Perhaps another way to describe this process is to imagine attempting to stick any object to a slippery surface. Anything stuck to a surface that is flooded with oil will sooner or later detach, similarly fat-soluble toxins will be released through this process. Whilst some cleansing programmes strive primarily to eliminate the water-soluble toxins in the body, the internal administration of medicated ghee targets the fat-soluble toxins to be released from the deeper tissues where they are lodged and contribute to the disease process.

What is important at this stage is to remember that you will be taking medicated ghee whilst being on a restricted diet. When you are on a low carbohydrate diet, the intake of fat works to your advantage as it increases the metabolic rate and even promotes fat loss. Interestingly, throughout my practice over the last twenty-five years, it is when my clients are in this phase of drinking medicated ghee, with a restricted diet for a short period of time, that they report best health, improved digestion and fat loss; almost a positive turning point on one's Ayurvedic journey. I understand if your concern is about eating fat on a regular basis whilst also eating carbohydrate rich food, this certainly would be a disastrous recipe. Also, the administration of medicated ghee is for such a short period of time, ranging anywhere between three to seven days, that it is an essential therapeutic diet and not a lifestyle.

Each stage of your Panchakarma journey requires close monitoring and supervision by an experienced Ayurvedic practitioner. In order for this deep cleansing process to go smoothly and without complications, it is essential to assess your progress and make any necessary changes, specifically during the days where you take medicated ghee as well as on the laxative day. Ideally, a daily assessment of your pulse and physiological rhythms will determine the dosage of ghee on the following day. This assessment can take place at the clinic or during home visits, depending on the number of scheduled ghee days.

After the initial ghee days, you will receive an Ayurvedic oil massage followed by a steam bath. The massage further brings the lipid soluble toxins into circulation. This process is supported by the application of heat, which dilates the blood vessels and helps to transport the toxins to the gastrointestinal tract. This initial stage of your preparation for Panchakarma culminates with a laxative day, followed by a specific diet to rekindle your digestion slowly, all of which are aspects of Method 5.

The taking of ghee, followed by the laxative day, may be repeated on a regular basis at two to three month intervals as recommended by your practitioner, which further prepares you for the ultimate seven to ten day residential Panchakarma retreat.

METHOD 5 - Panchakarma

Once you have undergone all procedures in Methods 4, Method 5 mainly achieves cleansing through administration of a laxative, a procedure that involves a whole day, ideally the first day or the second day of a residential retreat.

Having mobilised and eliminated both accumulated fat and water-soluble toxic waste from the deeper tissues in Method 4, the purpose of this retreat is to facilitate the healing process and to further encourage tissue repair. This is essential to help reverse the stages of the disease process as discussed in Chapter Two.

The uniqueness of such a retreat is to help you establish your natural rhythm, as well as to receive specific and prescriptive Ayurvedic body treatments, most of which are only appropriate within such a retreat setting. In addition to this, daily yoga, meditation sessions and food prepared using Ayurvedic principles strongly re-enforce, reconnect to and harmonise all the five elemental bodies and their innate ability to heal. The final stage of your Panchakarma is to receive a specifically prepared Ayurvedic herbal paste, the purpose of which is to build, nourish and strengthen your body. Most people continue to feel better and better long after the end of such a retreat, and they are then encouraged to maintain this newly found state of wellbeing.

The process of cleansing is a very essential task, and despite resulting in greater calmness, relaxation and improved wellbeing, it is also a delicate stage as the body will have worked very hard to detox. It is therefore important to allow enough time for this process and to follow the instructions of Panchakarma carefully, to rebuild resources so the physiological functions not only return to normal, but become sharper and more effective.

METHOD 6 - Maintenance Programme

Now that a proper Panchakarma has been carried out, be it for health-maintenance or for addressing specific health issues, a number of things could be done to sustain the effect of Panchakarma and to extend the benefits to long-lasting improved health.

This involves one or several of the following options:

- regular Ayurvedic check-ups
- receiving specific Ayurvedic therapies as recommended by the practitioner, especially the *Ayuwave* Marma Therapy
- proper use of self-help tools including yoga and meditation
- continued training in Ayurvedic methods of health care through educational workshops such as Ayurvedic food therapy, stress management (see www.ayuwave.com for more details).

The wonderful thing about Ayurveda is that you could consider using special herbal preparations that for thousands of years have been known to prevent illnesses and slow down ageing. Or you can take advantage of the sister sciences such as: Ayurvedic Astrology; the use of primordial sounds through

Vedic Mantras; incorporating energetic interior design through Vastu; and many other holistic approaches beyond physical health that can extend into other aspects of your life such as your home, garden and community.

Health and wellbeing are not all about cleansing, detoxing, purifying and repairing. If this is what health was all about, it would sound like a punishment. On the other hand, health and wellbeing are strongly influenced by every stimulus that our external senses are exposed to and the interpretation of those in our minds and emotions. If someone with a perfect digestion, a very fit body, and a bright and intelligent mind has to work in an office with no view, no windows and an annoying colleague, their experience of wellbeing would be extremely poor despite ticking all the boxes of good health. The environments that we live and work in, the colours we see, the clothes we wear and the scents we smell all have a major impact on expanding or constricting the feeling of wellbeing. Therefore, in Chapter Five I will provide useful tips on how to maintain sensory and emotional wellbeing by choosing the right colours, uplifting aromas and feel-good self-care rituals. For example, most coffee lovers don't drink coffee for its caffeine but to enjoy every aspect of the coffee drinking ritual–very similar to the Japanese tea party that is more about the ritual than the tea itself. The best coffee in town drunk in a crowded, shabby and smelly place will not give the same experience that the ritual does. Funnily enough, sometimes the content of life is only as good as the container. At times ordinary coffee or tea in your favourite cup gives you the same great feeling. This is perhaps what medicine calls a placebo; however, placebos do have a great benefit.

From a holistic perspective everything matters as we are multi-layered. Our bodies are as good as our emotions, and our emotions are as good as our external environment. Interestingly, each of us are gifted to recognise one or two of our layers; but developing an understanding of all that we are made of is a wonderful way to achieve balance quickly and to maintain permanently. The next section of this chapter introduces you to these multiple layers and how you can influence health or create illness.

The Five Bodies

As discussed in *Chapter One–Awareness*, you define yourself based on trained sensory experiences and stored memories, which trigger you to act or respond in a certain way. However, for thousands of years yogis have acknowledged that there are several layers to who you are as a human being, which go beyond what your senses can perceive, your mind can think or your intellect is able to recognise. Your body is the most obvious layer that can be felt, touched, seen and has a distinct smell, therefore the most real one.

'Natural health' as seen from the five-body perspective is when your:

- *physical* body is in a state of optimal health
- *energy* body maintains an increased frequency
- *mental* body is in a state where peace of mind is assured
- *emotional* body is in balance
- *awareness* body is in alignment with a higher intelligence that activates self-repair.

In summary, your existence is far more than matter and intelligence; it extends to five bodies, which again can be linked to the five elements.

Your Physical or Earth Body

The dense physical body is the grossest of all the five bodies, it is the physical self, which is nourished by food throughout life and after death goes back into earth. Therefore, it can be related to the element of earth. This earth body has a well-defined, specific physical structure that is tangible, consisting of skin, muscles, joints and bones, for example. In functional medicine, optimal physical health can be measured in terms of a balanced functioning and harmonious interaction of all the bodily systems, such as your digestive, endocrine, nervous, respiratory and your immune system.

In situations when my body feels run down or when I fall sick, I appreciate 'the gift of absence'. Health is often taken for granted and many of my clients, including myself, have the tendency to treat the body like a piece of soap– the more it's used, the more it wears down. This seems to be acceptable for

> *"Take care of your body; it is the only place you have to live."*
>
> *Jim Rohn*

a long time, strangely enough. It is only when the soap seems to fade in front of our eyes, in the absence of health, where the importance of it can be felt.

The physical body is like a temple that should be nurtured and treated with care.

Over the last ten years or so, I have undergone Panchakarma on a regular basis at least once a year. Each kept me going for another decade and helped me immensely to cope with excessive travel and many uncertainties and stresses in life. About two years ago, I felt my liver becoming toxic again. I slowly started to put on weight, my sleep got disturbed and I developed a stubborn cyst on my right eye, which didn't want to go away, even after trying all sorts of potions and packs. It was then that I paused and reflected upon how I had neglected my physical health. How could I have expected my body to just keep going, like a steam train, without fuelling its engine?

Sadly, many of us in the health field are our own worst patient. We disregard our physical need for rest and repair. It still took me almost another six months before I booked myself into an Ayurvedic retreat, where seven days of total cleansing, rest and repair fortunately turned my health around again.

What I am trying to say is that we can't operate on a daily basis without a healthy body; without a clean machine that effortlessly transforms food into energy; where the bodies biochemistry synthesises protein to make up or repair parts of the body; where insulin helps in the metabolism of glucose; where the kidney filters impurities from the blood; and where proper release of thyroxin results in a health metabolism and a million other biochemical processes.

Keeping all that in mind, the best lymph drainage system that keeps the 'dustbin' clean, the best supplements and medicines, the most effective anti-parasite programme, colon cleanse, body treatments and the best organic food will *not* work in the long run to keep you healthy without considering the other four subtler bodies, which are less obvious and tangible, but under no circumstances can be neglected.

In my clinical practice I emphasise the need to create change from the outside in. By outside I mean the subtler, finer levels of the body and by treating these parallel to the physical body, my clients are able to see results on their journey to wellbeing and come closer to achieving their goal of optimal health.

Your Energy or Fire Body

Now that we have looked at the 'physical or earth body' and what optimal physical health means, just imagine if you could perceive the body behind the body, what would you see?

First of all you would see the underlying energy structure that gives life to your physical body, which could be described as your aura. This aura or energetic field is not static, it constantly changes with every thought you think, every action you do and every emotion you feel. It is the breath of life that enters your body at the time of conception and the last whiff that leaves your body at the time of death.

The breath of life or Prana is both the physical breath that fills your lungs and enriches your blood with oxygen, and the subtle life energy of the body. For example, there is a difference between the desire and mental intention to adopt a healthier lifestyle and the effort and determination to make changes to your lifestyle that could improve your health and wellbeing. Prana unites or links the mind to the form or body so that it can function in it. In this way, Prana controls and activates all bodily processes, the mind's capacity to make sensible decisions, the ability to love or hate, increased awareness and your power to connect with your higher self. Health or disease, happiness or despair, ageing or rejuvenation are all dependent on the healthy flow of Prana.

Prana is the life force that strings body, mind and spirit
together like beads on a strand.

Just as food and nutrients flow through the body in physical pathways, Prana flows in invisible channels, and this is what makes up the entirety of the 'energy body'. This energy body is like a light bulb that radiates outwards and emanates light beyond the bulb. It is not static; it expands and contracts.

Whenever there is obstruction or interruption of the flow of Prana, the energy body contracts. This contraction leads to a drop in frequency and when this frequency falls below 62 hertz, as established by Dr Royal Rife in the 1930s and discussed in detail in chapter one, when unaddressed for an extended period of time provides the starting point of any disease process. On the other hand, by eating foods that are full of Prana, for example, freshly prepared and unprocessed foods, your energy body expands. This could be enough to maintain the body's frequency within its normal range, ensuring a good state of health, or at least this could provide a starting point to turn your health around.

Your energy or fire body, as one of the four subtler bodies, is the gatekeeper between your physical body and the other three subtler bodies. In my clinical practice as a holistic health practitioner, one of the approaches to achieve improved health and wellbeing is to keep the body frequency at optimal levels, which allows permanent access to the Matrix, where natural health can become a living reality.

Your Mental Body and the Element of Air

Ayurveda understands that the element of air manifests as the worries and sorrows of the mind. Your mind moves as quickly as air. You think approximately 70,000 thoughts a day, which equates to about forty-eight thoughts a minute. Trying to control the mind is like attempting to tame a wild animal. It requires discipline and patience. In this section I discuss how behavioural patterns form, as well as the importance of keeping your mental body in a state of peace and calm.

Your mental body is the vehicle through which the higher self-manifests as individual self, the 'concrete mind'. Your concrete mind forms slowly over years from the time of birth. Eventually, it makes up your character based on adopted or learned behavioural patterns as you grow up. On a day-to-day basis it is not just your character or acquired behaviour that affect your decisions, but perhaps more important is the state of your mind, which influences the decision making process at any given moment.

There are three states of the mind:

- the mind when it is peaceful
- the mind when it is overactive
- the mind when it is tired.

I remember many years ago I was teaching at a Vedic school in Thailand. It was one of my first trips to Asia and during my stay in Bangkok I had immense difficulties in adjusting to the new environment. I struggled with my health and could hardly get any quality sleep because of the heat, humidity and the ever so annoying attacks by mosquitos, which seemed to enjoy sucking my blood, especially at night time. Over a period of five weeks, despite having eaten lots of delicious, hot and healthy prepared Thai food, I kept losing more and more weight and by the time I came home, it was like I no longer was 'carrying' a suit but the suit was 'carrying' me, hung on a far too small coat hanger. My cravings for a nice piece of homemade cake intensified as time went on and the first thing I did, when arriving back in Europe, was to go to a bakery and indulge myself in a few pieces of homemade cake. I deliberately say 'a few pieces' since I feel a bit embarrassed to tell you how many I actually had…I did not care about the consequences of my cake indulgence at the time, but you probably can imagine how I felt soon after.

What led me to overindulge then?

Because I was so tired mentally, I did not care about the consequences of eating that amount cake at once while I was eating it in the café. At the time I didn't think about the need to make a decision, I just went ahead and did it anyway. Perhaps it was an impulsive reaction due to my mental exhaustion. This is what Sigmund Freud probably meant by the irrational and emotional part of the mind, which says, "I want something and I want it now."

Let's just look at how my actions could have been different had my mind been in an overactive state. Before indulging in the cake eating process I would have argued why it was necessary for me to have the cake. For example, "Oh, you deserve it since you haven't had any for such a long time", or "You have lost so much weight you can afford to eat whatever you like". So in that state, the mind looks for justification as to why a particular decision should be made. As Freud says: the rational part that develops through reasoning and out of the need for negotiation. *I want it because I need it.* Had I been in that overactive state, it probably would not have stopped there. I probably would have been in a constant dilemma, arguing in my head the pros and cons of eating the cake and, independently of what decision I had made, I still would doubt my decision. Eating or not eating, one or five pieces, I would have felt unhappy irrespective of the decision I made at that moment.

However, the mind in a peaceful state would convince me that it is perfectly all right to have some cake at this moment. Eating cake then is not because of urgency or greediness, but I would have seen it as a treat and I felt more in control of the decision and would have been happy with it.

When your mind is in a more peaceful state, your habits are more likely to shift naturally.

On a daily basis an average adult makes more than 30,000 decisions. Some of them are voluntary; small one's where you consciously choose things like where to sit or what to wear. However, most of the decisions are involuntary, in which your brain sends messages to your body to follow or respond to and vice versa; for example, the secretion of digestive juices and your heart rate. But it is not about the number of decisions, it is the accumulative consequences, in particular, of those voluntary decisions you make on a daily basis. If every decision you make is in a conflict or causing stress, for example, you forgot your mobile, took the wrong key, haven't topped up your travel card and ended up paying a fine. This is very likely to be a reflection of a high degree of tiredness. Also, in that state, by the time you are able to sit down and relax in the evening, you may be more likely to grab hold of a chocolate bar; even though you have decided to start losing weight, or have half a bottle of wine, despite your desire to reduce your alcohol consumption during the week. On the other hand, if your mind is calm and peaceful, you probably would make more beneficial decisions such as listening to some music or playing with your children in order to relax. A way to measure if your mental body is in a balanced state is exactly that experience of mental peace, a sense of contentment, which provides an important platform for health and wellbeing. So the key is to shift your state of mind from a tired or overactive state to a more peaceful state. When you are in that space, your habits are more likely to shift naturally.

Shift your state of mind and then your habits shift more naturally.

It is the state of mind you are in at the time when making any decision that will determine the winner of the psychological battle over habits. In order for you to be able to break habits, you need to get into a more calm state of mind, as this will provide the basis to reconstruct your brain towards more positive behaviours.

How Are Bad Habits Formed?

As discussed in the previous paragraph, the state of your mind very much influences the decisions you make. If your mind is tired, you might interpret things that are normally useful as being harmful and you might see that which is harmful as being useful. This is how, for example, for some people eating freshly prepared vegetables can be seen as unsuitable and having fast food is what they eat instead. What has led to that confusion? The answer lies in the relationship between the mind and the brain.

False messages can lead to the formation of unwanted habits.

The brain is like the hardware of your computer and that hardware needs software to make it run, which is your mind. The brain is an organ but the mind isn't. Commonly understood, the brain is the physical place where the mind resides. The brain is a vessel in which the electronic impulses that create thought are contained and responded to. Those thoughts or impulses that arise from a restful mind help to bring you closer to your true goals and intentions in life, closer to your true self, leading to decisions that are supportive and helpful. On the other hand, when your mind is tired or overactive, the brain receives false messages that lead to more destructive habits. Using the example of one of my clients, despite having beautiful features and a figure that some can only dream of, her impression of herself was that she was ugly and therefore everyone rejected her, which was the main reason for her depression resulting in a disturbed relationship towards food.

What Is Hebb's Law?

Hebb's Law states that when nerve cells are activated in the same pattern repeatedly, they eventually form a brain circuit. As a result, areas that are involved in this circuit respond in the same way every time a similar situation arises. You may have heard about Pavlov's dog experiment. Ring a bell and the dog doesn't salivate. Show food to the dog, and the dog starts salivating. Ring the bell along with showing the food, and the dog salivates. Ring the bell and the dog salivates. What is happening is called synchronisation. At first, there is a weak or no association between a bell and food. The two stimuli operate independently of each other in their synaptic firing. As the two stimuli continue to be active at the same time, the synapses between them are strengthened or created, and they begin to fire in unison.

Neurons that fire together wire together.

Why is it So Hard to Break Bad Habits?

Looking at bad habits from a pure physiological perspective, one might say that perhaps lack of Vitamin B and magnesium could be the cause for habitual indulgence in chocolate, or low calcium could lead to increased consumption of alcohol, and by correcting the mineral imbalance, we are able to break those habits. However, in reality it is a bit more complicated.

The more often you feed unhealthy messages, the stronger you will carve the link to harmful and unhealthy behaviours.

Whenever you respond in the same way repeatedly to a destructive brain message, by focusing on and engaging in an unhealthy habit –for example, drinking half a bottle of wine when stressed– you essentially teach the brain to always respond in the same way. The more often you feed these unhealthy or wrong messages–*I am ugly; I am not good enough; I am totally stressed; There is something wrong with me* and so on– the stronger you will carve the link to harmful and unhealthy behaviours. Your response becomes hardwired and you will start engaging in harmful behaviour without even realising it. On top of that, your repeated action strengthens the brain circuit, which, for example, could be linked to the consumption of alcohol or a reaction of anger as a response to external criticism, lack of attention or when feeling overwhelmed.

Take another example: your subconscious might remember that your mum always gave you food when you felt upset. With this memory, over time having food becomes an automatic response to feeling upset. Slowly that brain circuit gets strengthened and before you know it, you might be addicted to food.

So in summary, focused attention is like glue that holds together particular parts of the brain so they can keep communicating with each other. The more you repeat certain thoughts, the denser your attention is and, as a result, the more likely a specific habit will be wired into your brain. It then becomes like a line scratched in a piece of rock, which is difficult to erase.

How to Break Habits?

According to Ram Dass, human beings were born into this world from a place of safety and shelter, and when entering their new existence this memory of 'feeling at home' is very much alive. It is only when, for whatever reason, we get separated from this feeling that we start to experience pain, mostly emotional. As a result, any actions we take are with the intention to help us get back 'home'.

In essence there are only two feelings that motivate us to act, either pleasure or pain. When you, for example, grab hold of a bottle of wine to make up for your feeling of not being loved, it might be to change your sensation of pain into a feeling of pleasure. Drinking wine at that moment will take away the feeling of separateness and the short rush you get will bring temporarily pleasure. However, perhaps the next morning, when you are able to stand back and reflect on the night before, you will see the predicament and the short term pleasure will have transformed quickly into a more long-term pain.

Just ask yourself this question: why do many programmes that claim to be able to get people off their addictions perhaps succeed short-term but often fail in the long run? This is because the programme itself becomes a new addiction. Comments like, "Oh, I have managed to keep off cigarettes now for one year, two months and twenty-seven days", show that they are still thinking about their addiction and the problem is not truly solved.

Were you able to get off your addictions short-term but did you fail in the long run?

In my clinical practice I take a different approach. One of my clients came to seek advice because of symptoms of stress, her inability to sleep and its effect on her digestion. Over a period of six months, she took specific Ayurvedic remedies and lifestyle advice. Also she learned many of the self-help techniques as described in the next chapter, which allowed her to increase self-awareness. She found a way of managing her stressful life by connecting to her higher self. At some point during a follow up session, she mentioned that a pleasant side effect of the Ayurvedic treatment programme was that it saved her a lot of money. Initially I didn't understand, and then she shared how, by embarking on the Ayurvedic journey, she was able to overcome her internet shopping addiction as a way to manage her stress.

"Whenever I felt stressed," she explained, "I would go for gratification by buying myself a treat for all the hard work." Consequently, as she was about to open the computer, her brain would set in motion the whole sequence again and she couldn't stop herself from internet shopping.

If you are in a similar situation, please don't beat yourself up when you have made efforts to try to change a habit and failed. Start by increasing your awareness to break the chain of reactivity. Heightened awareness allows you to see yourself in a different way. If you want to change your habits, keep cultivating new practices by choosing where to focus your attention. For example, if feeling stressed, take a warm bath or talk to a close friend. Through repetition, apply this new way of reacting to your feeling of 'being unloved'. By retraining your brain with a more wholesome and constructive activity, you will herewith create new neurological pathways that eventually will reconstruct your brain in ways that are healthier and in alignment with your true self. By doing so, you will create that 'coming back home' feeling of safety and contentment.

Retrain your brain with wholesome and constructive activities.

Jeffrey M. Schwartz discusses this whole process of how to rewire your brain in great detail in his book, *You Are Not Your Brain*. He mentions that you are not in control of your false, or what he calls 'deceptive messages', but your brain is. This means you cannot make, for example, the sensation of 'not being good enough' or 'not feeling loved' or 'having physical cravings for something' go away by using willpower or positive thinking alone.

This knowing is not enough to turn a corner and to change a certain behaviour. Trying to do so is a recipe of failure. Repeated behavioural patterns form distinct neurological pathways, which are physiological events that can only be changed through repeated effort.

In addition you have to find techniques to tame your mind:

- Cultivate a peaceful state of mind by practising techniques that get you in touch **with your higher self.**
- When you are in that state, rewire your brain through repeated re-focusing.

In *Chapter Four* I will describe the '*Ayuvwave OBC*' Technique, a step-by-step process that will assist you in reconstructing new pathways in your brain, and many effective self-help procedures that can become extremely valuable tools to tame 'the wild animal' – your mind.

Your Emotional Body and the Element of Water

Whenever someone walks through the door of my clinic, one of the first questions I ask is, "What has made you come and seek help today?" In 99.9% of the cases the answer would be something along the lines of:

- "I experience some pain in my stomach each time I eat."
- "I can't sleep."
- "I don't seem to be able to lose weight."

Perhaps you would agree that it is usually any type of physical discomfort such as pain, fatigue, allergies or an unhealthy skin that is the trigger and makes you seek advice from a health professional. It is only when I take my clients through the five body assessment process using pulse and tongue analysis, and when I then explain that the root cause of their physical problem lies in one of the four subtler bodies, for example, in the emotional body, that my clients look at me and say, "This makes so much sense. I never thought that my emotional discomfort could have such an impact on my physical wellbeing".

How long have you ignored the emotional splinter under your nail?

If you had a splinter under your fingernail, would you ignore it? Yet how long have you been able to walk around with an emotional splinter and disregarded its effect on your health? Whenever you feel any negative emotion, your emotional body is in pain and anguish, crying out for help. It is a sign that you have lost connection to your highest self, which is the storehouse of all positive and life-supporting emotions such as contentment, gratitude, trust and love. In the same way as you need to keep your physical body subtle and free from toxins, you need to ensure you keep your emotional body flexible and pleasing to experience.

Your emotional body is linked to the element of water and is one of the main bodies that, when worked upon and some clearing has been done, will affect and improve your overall state of wellbeing. In essence, the emotional body is energy in nature, where all sensations you might currently experience or which you have experienced in the past are automatically stored. Effortless, without thinking, any emotion or sensation is sent directly to your emotional body, which is the wireless, automatic backup hardware of your 'computer'.

Over time you begin to operate with a full emotional storage bin, which influences all your thoughts, the way you speak and your actions. However, the aim should not be to store emotions there permanently, but instead release these feelings so you can move forward and stay in the present, without attached baggage from the past. If you have a healthy emotional body, you will be able to live in the here and now. If not, you tend to live in the past or in the future.

I have to admit that even after years of meditation practice, personal development and an interesting journey towards self-discovery that forced me to have faith and trust in the 'unknown'– especially during times of adversities and uncertainties– to clear the emotional body from any baggage is certainly not as straightforward and simple as it sounds.

In this context, I wish to share an incident with you that occurred recently, just whilst writing this particular chapter of the book. Someone very close to me freely expressed how I had wasted the prime time of my life, my early twenties, 'hiding away' in a secluded residence somewhere in the mountains of Switzerland while 'blindly following' a guru and being involved in a spiritual organisation where there was no space for independent views and thinking. The work was voluntary work with no social security or financial income. 'And all for what?'

Whilst I was listening to this, I could feel a wave of anger and frustration washing over me. All my spiritual practices went out of the window, and before I realised what was going on, I could not control my emotions and reacted in a defensive manner. It is best not to go into the details of that verbal fight. Later, once the waters had calmed again, it occurred to me that I was responding to the present situation, not based on what was going on *now* but what went on a long time ago. I could hear my father's voice when this person was expressing to me his concerns about me losing myself in what he thought had been a religious community, with no money, when I could have had such a bright career by now if I had kept my secure position as an administrator working for the government.

Any emotional pain, trauma, shock or even positive emotions are stored in the limbic system of our brain. The limbic system is the collective name for structures in the human brain involved in emotions, in particular those related to survival such as fear and anger or those experienced when eating or having sex. Certain parts of the limbic system are also involved with memory and its emotional association. Depending on how huge an emotional response a particular event invokes or has invoked in the past, these memories will be sent to a particular part of the limbic system for long-term storage from where they can be retrieved when necessary.

The limbic system is not only the seat of emotion; it is often also called the 'nose' brain because it connects directly to the olfactory receptors. According to the German parfumeur and flavourist Jellinek, odours are experienced within the context of life situations. This means that if you experience a particular smell within a highly charged emotional situation, then the emotions experienced are stored alongside the odour experience. If at any later stage you come across the same particular smell, this will trigger its associated stored emotion. A smell can bring a flood of memories, influence your mood and even affect your work performance.

> *"Odours are experienced within the context of life situations."*
>
> *Jellinek*

Although today I consider myself a 'free spirit' who does not belong to any particular religion, the memory of a shy and timid altar boy is tucked away in the smell of frankincense, taking me right back to happy childhood moments where I got to wear a black cassock, which is a beautiful, flowing floor-length robe with lots of buttons down the front. (Well, my 'career' as an altar boy ended when I was caught drinking the 'mass wine' out of a chalice) …

On the other hand, the smell of eucalyptus used to make me sick because it reminded me of a horrible tasting cough medicine my mum gave to me as a child when I was recovering from a chest infection. Whilst living in Australia in the late 1990s' I could not escape that smell and therefore was finally able to clear the memory and associated stored emotions.

In *Chapter Four* I will explain several techniques and processes that can be used to clear the emotional body, such as the *Ayuwave* Marma Therapy, Vedic Meditation and the use of specific essential oils. Over years of clinical experience, these simple but highly effective tools have proven to be helpful in erasing stored negative emotions; not by re-living the trauma or the shock, which can often be a traumatic experience in itself, but in a gentle and subtle way. In this way, specific therapies and techniques become the Matrix that connects you to your higher self, which then automatically clears your emotional body and activates your innate healing ability.

Your Awareness Body and the Element of Space

Trying to improve health without awareness is like driving a car without fuel; you won't get anywhere.

The first chapter of this book, *Awareness– the Foundation to Health and Wellbeing,* explained in great depth the role of awareness on anybody who chooses to embark on the health journey and why it can be related to the element of space. Therefore, I won't repeat what has been discussed earlier. But I do encourage you to go back and re-read some of the sections to refresh your memory.

Trying to improve health without awareness is like driving a car without fuel; you won't get anywhere. Health awareness begins with small steps, for example, becoming conscious of your sleeping and eating patterns, how you feel at different times of the day and how you respond to what is said in certain circumstances. These observations and the mere thought of wanting to become aware, combined with all the techniques and suggestions described in the next chapter, will not only help you to touch base with your individual self, the person who you truly are, but it will also connect you to a force that extends beyond the 'you'. By allowing that heightened awareness to come to life, you join hands with the healer within who associates with you and guides you in the right direction; who connects you with the right people at the right time that can be of help to you, so you can live the life you deserve, where nobody else but you can take charge of your health.

The Five Elemental Bodies Interacting

For any health-related transformation to be permanent, it has to happen from the outside in. This means creating change in one or all of the subtler bodies first, which then will speed up the healing process and enhance any programme with a predominantly 'earth body' focus. Of course, in chronic conditions and in clients with more serious health challenges, one has to work on the earth body as well as on the other elemental bodies simultaneously.

A transformation of your health has to happen from the outside in.

I wasn't thinking that way at all when I started as an Ayurvedic practitioner. At that time, I was fixed on the dos and don'ts of an ideal Ayurvedic diet, the prescription of herbs and spices and the planning of individually tailored cleansing programmes. Also, each client I saw left the clinic with some advice on how to re-align his or her circadian rhythm. It was only later in my practice, after questioning and analysing as to why some of my clients found it easier to follow the given instructions than others, when I developed the concept of the *Ayuwave* Five Body Assessment. I noticed that in principle clients mostly started the consultation by using one of the five different modes below when expressing and explaining their health concerns:

- "I feel…"
- "I think…"
- "I have…"
- "I am…"
- "I trust…"

These five modes of expression can be related easily to the five bodies.

The *emotional body* for example, would say, "**I feel** frustrated because I can't sleep".

A client, predominantly in their *mental body*, would say, "**I think** my problem is because I have food intolerance".

Anyone mostly in touch with his or her *physical body* would express any health concerns more as a matter of fact: "**I have** indigestion or I have a problem with my back."

"**I am** really tired", indicates to me a relation to the *energetic body*.

Those who are in touch with their *individual self or even higher self* would in one way or the other mention during the consultation, "**I trust** I will be fine" or "**I sense** that I would need to do some detoxification".

A good practitioner listens with an open mind and without a trace of judgment.

One of the main qualities a good practitioner should have is the ability to listen with an open mind and without a trace of judgement. Good listening helps tremendously in deciding the course of action for a successful treatment. Once I have established which 'body' my client is mainly using or most familiar with, then I will know exactly what language to best communicate in so I can be understood, and my client is more likely to follow through what has been suggested. Let me share one of my clinical cases and the treatment approach I took, which hopefully will help to clarify the above concept.

About one and a half years ago, a fifty-eight-year-old male, an extremely busy businessman, was referred to me by one of my colleagues. He came with a clear idea in mind that he wanted to experience a Marma Therapy, through which apparently his wife had experienced such a deep healing. Although I tried to convince him that it was essential to have a brief Five Body Assessment first, he insisted that he just wanted the Marma Therapy, nothing else. I did the treatment and afterwards, when I asked him to share his experience of the treatment, he was very disappointed and disliked what he called the 'flowery massage'. He could not wait until the hour was up and it was time for him to get off the treatment table. Interestingly, the same person came back about six months later because of a gradually worsening health issue. This time I sat down and spent the first thirty minutes doing my Five Body Assessment and explained in detail how the suggested Marma treatment would work. Although I had recognised the need for him to understand the process during his first visit, I had obliged him in his wish to receive the Marma Therapy without much explanation, which resulted in non-transfer of the effect of the treatment on him.

It is in such instances, where a person who functions predominantly from the physical and mental bodies would need a primer by explaining the process and the possible outcomes for the treatment to be effective. On the other hand, another client of mine, in a similar situation with the same health condition, found it hard to focus on anything for more than three seconds, so I decided to start with Marma Therapy as the very first procedure before I did my detailed consultation. This time it worked perfectly because this client was largely in touch with her emotional body and needed the interjection of Marma Therapy to make the connection to her physical and mental body. Once this connection was established through Marma Therapy, I was able to gain her full attention during the actual health consultation.

In essence, approaching a client for establishing balance is like identifying the most important point, similar to when trying to unknot a thread that has multiple knots. Once the key point is detected and dealt with, all other knots seem to untwine effortlessly. On the contrary, trying to unknot a thread randomly can lead to frustration and may, in fact, knot the thread even more. Therefore, I see the need to assess all the five bodies and when they are being addressed in the treatment protocol holistically, the person can yield to receiving the benefits with least resistance. The ultimate goal in my practice is to have the five bodies work together in close harmony with each other, without obstruction of the flow of Prana, where improved health and a great sense of wellbeing will be a natural result.

"Thanks so much for picking up a stranger, someone you just met a couple of weeks ago. I need to tell you what had happened to me. I feel a bit lost now, not knowing what to do once I arrive in New Zealand," I explained.

"Don't worry, something will work out. Just go and rest here for a couple of days. Enjoy Noosa, the sun and beach; we will look after you."

A couple of days later, one morning after breakfast I was called into the office to listen to a phone conversation between my friend and someone else on the other end of the phone...

"Oh, how interesting, did you say he is an Ayurvedic Practitioner? I think I might have seen his advert in the local paper, looking for a job. Thomas, did you place an ad into a paper in New Zealand?" No, I am sorry, but this must be a misunderstanding because I haven't placed any ad into any paper in New Zealand. Though I have got the paper here... The Green Clinic in the Bay of Plenty, is currently looking for an Ayurvedic Practitioner to join their team of health professionals. This is the number, just ask Thomas to ring the lady and talk to her.

When I rang the number, the lady on the other line said: "Oh, so you are the person I was meant to meet and I was given instructions form 'above' to sponsor and to help into the country? When can I meet you?"

Within two weeks I had my New Zealand work permit. And the rest is history... Looking back it was even better than I could ever have imagined or anyone could have organised. Perhaps, I would say nature at its perfection. Limitations only exist in our minds. I fully trusted the process and was open to receive, without much resistance. My journey to understanding that wellbeing starts not on a physical level but much higher.

Irrespective of where you start your Ayurvedic journey, or what your motives are to use the Ayurvedic approach to improving your health and wellbeing, it is very much about having the faith and trust in the process. This 'inner knowing' is a sign of attunement with your higher self, which will guide and support you until you have achieved the desired outcome. Similar to my personal story at the beginning of this chapter, most of the time it is unclear as to where the expedition takes you, which challenges come along your way and which detours you might have to take. But it is your unshaken belief and trust in the journey that will encourage you to move forward and not to look back. Expect the unexpected and the right door will open at the right time. You will be surprised how all of a sudden you find the Matrix to Natural Health right there within you.

It is not necessarily about controlling the course but also accepting the need to let go and see where the natural flow of life will take you.

You find the Matrix to Natural Health right there within you.

The next chapter is the core of the book, which invites you to try out and play with the tools and techniques as described. They will become your instruments and have the potential to create a beautiful piece of music. Like the conductor of an orchestra, the self-repair mechanism once activated brings together all of the varying five bodies and their functions. And when they finally work in harmony, health, wellbeing and total youthfulness is inevitable.

What If

○ What if you were offered the secret to reduce your biological age and cellular degeneration whilst rejuvenating your entire being?

○ What if you allow yourself the time and permission for your body to heal?

○ What if you align your five bodies to naturally access the Matrix that will activate self-repair and rejuvenation?

Call to Action

If there is one therapy that you feel most drawn to, which one would that be and why?

Think about a conflict situation where you responded based not on what was going on at that moment, but rather on what went on a long time ago. Reflect upon which of the five modes of expression this scenario shows you use predominantly and how this informs your interactions with people.

Amrita – Nectar of the Natural Health Matrix:

- The ultimate path to good health is regular Panchakarma.

- Shift your state of mind and then your habits will shift naturally.

- The more often you feed unhealthy messages, the stronger you will carve the link to harmful and unhealthy behaviours.

- Cultivating health awareness begins with small steps such as observing your eating and sleeping patterns.

- A transformation of health has to happen from the outside in, from the subtler bodies to the gross physical body.

- The Matrix to Natural Health can be found there, right within you

FOUR ~ FIRE

The Power Of Transformation

"Michael, Michael, wake up, I don't know what is happening but I can't breathe."

"It's one-thirty in the morning; what's wrong?"

"I can't breathe and I have such a stabbing pain in my chest." I jumped up and stumbled out of the tent. Whilst walking in the fresh air, under Australia's most stunning skies and in the middle of the desert, everything seemed to calm down after a while.

What was that? I asked myself. Did I dream; a nightmare or perhaps a spider bite?

No...

I was mesmerised by the stars and for the first time in my life I could see the Milky Way moving in slow motion above my head. No artificial source of light, not a single cloud. The sparkling glitter above my head, the Southern Cross on my right and a small crescent moon to my left. The smell of freedom combined with the fear of the unknown. I felt something wasn't right at home, my dad. I knew what I had to do.

"I am off. I have to find a telephone box. I need to make a call..."

"...Mum, it's me. What's happening with Dad?" A trembling voice struggling for words on the other end of the line, 15,000 kilometres away, told me that my dad had been admitted to hospital after suffering from a severe heart attack. My dad recovered slowly, but it was only one

of many incidents that followed over the next eight years.

It was in winter 1999 in New Zealand, one of those miserable times of the year, with plenty of rain, cold and damp weather conditions and no central heating in most of the homes. Again, one night I woke up after just a couple of hours of sleep, with cold sweat on my forehead and a racing heart, shivering all over. No bad dream or at least not that I remembered. I didn't pay any attention and just as I was about to go back to sleep the phone rang.

"Why do you call me this late? What's going on?"

"Your dad again. This time it really seems serious. They had to put him into an induced coma to decrease brain activity and to reduce the swelling of the brain. It doesn't look too good and he probably won't make it this time."

"Oh no, I can't get away from here and even if I could, it would take me at least three days and it perhaps will be too late by then." I desperately tried to go back to sleep that night, but my head was spinning and I went through an intense phase of anger, frustration and anxiety, especially when contemplating the decision to take a flight next morning or to stay behind and wait. I was broke at the time, had no money to pay for an expensive flight and I was too proud to ask my family for help. If I didn't go and something happened to my dad, would I ever forgive myself?

In This Chapter We Discuss:

- How to strengthen your Agni and how to reduce Ama.
- How to stay emotionally calm and mentally cool.
- How to find your own natural rhythm.
- How to follow a balanced diet.

Why is This Chapter Called 'Fire'?

So far the previous chapters have looked at the concepts of space, earth and air, which to a great extent form the raw material for transformation. With many short-term and long-term transformations in nature, fire plays an important role. In fact, fire is almost the most important element necessary for any transformation to occur. For example, for a beautifully and carefully cast earthen pot made by a potter to become a useful container to store water, the intensity of fire is needed to burn it to become a strong earthen pot. In this sense, to change the concepts, the ideas and the processes from the previous chapters into the experience of health and wellbeing, it is important to ignite the fire of action, the exact methods of which will be described in this chapter.

How to Best Use This Chapter

This chapter is full of practical tips. It gives a comprehensive explanation of nutrition, detoxification, mind-body practices, energetic techniques and everything else that forms the toolkit for perfect health and wellbeing. Just as a child, when taken in to a theme park, can become completely overwhelmed due to the speed and variety of choices, I wouldn't be surprised if some of you become overwhelmed as to where to start, which aspects to choose and how to coordinate the various activities described in this chapter. Considering this, I have provided colour coding for each suggestion and the advice then relates to the five elements, which represent the different dimensions, from where you could choose to work.

For the benefit of easy application, the five colours in the following paragraphs relate to the five elements (space, air, fire, water and earth), which in turn relate to the five bodies (awareness, mental, energetic, emotional and physical).

Colour-coded keys for this chapter:

Awareness body - Space

Mental body – Air

Energetic body – Fire

Emotional body – Water

Physical body – Earth

For instance, if you want to work on the energetic body, you could choose one or several of the suggestions marked in the colour 'red'. On the other hand, if you choose to work on the physical body, choose the sections marked in 'yellow'. They are organised in the table in order of importance. For instance, if the yellow square is first in the table, followed by the triangle and the circle, this indicates that the particular recommendation acts predominantly on the physical body, secondary on the energetic body and to some extent on the mental body.

> *"If you always do what you have always done, you will always get what you have always got."*
>
> Dan Hayes

Remember the question I asked at the beginning of this book? "Do you live life or is life living you?" This chapter is an invitation to embrace change and I encourage you to take charge of your health by doing things differently from how you might have done them in the past. Some of these suggestions may first appear a bit unusual or different, and again I ask you to trust the process and try them out. Only then will you be able to notice the difference these suggestions can make to your health.

As this chapter explains all practical aspects, it can be used as a stand-alone manual that will help you to towards an experience of improved health and wellbeing. To optimise the information contained in this chapter, you might perhaps go back to *Chapter Two– Key Concepts of Ayurvedic Health* and refresh your memory on the three Doshas or bio-energetic principles. Based on the outcome of the bio-individuality self-assessment, I recommend specific approaches for Vata, Pitta or Kapha personalities. If you don't know your bio-individuality, go to www.NaturalHealthMatrix.com and download your free assessment form.

As a Vata personality, you may have the tendency to get all excited and want to do everything at the same time. But the challenge with Vata is they get bored easily. Therefore, I suggest you pick only one aspect of the self-help tools related to any of the five bodies as mentioned in this chapter. Choose the one that appeals most to you and incorporate that change or use that technique in your daily life for a couple of weeks and then slowly build your tool kit by introducing other aspects.

If your predominant bio-individuality is Pitta, generally speaking your ability to organise and to structure your daily life might allow you to include most of the tools mentioned in this section of the book from the very beginning. However, after a while you may find yourself getting stressed, and then the de-stressing techniques and procedures become the actual stressors, which defeats the purpose. It is for this reason that I like you to take a more relaxed approach, where less is more.

Out of all of the three Doshas, as a Kapha personality you will find it most challenging to allow change into your life. "Tomorrow I will start," might be your favourite saying. If that is the case, just remember that there is no point waiting for the right moment, since that moment is never going to come. To keep motivated and to stay inspired, choose a close friend to be your 'health buddy' with whom you can share the various steps of your Ayurvedic journey. Ask that person to motivate you should you feel down or lack inspiration. Don't be afraid to ask someone to hold your hand at the beginning. Once the experience of improved health and wellbeing is locked into your cellular memory, you won't look back and your determination will carry you forward.

The Only Actions You Will Ever Need To Take to Strengthen Your Agni and Reduce Ama

Fire, the flame of desire and passion, the blaze that is able to transform, change, destroy and create; nothing in life moves or can exist without that fuel or Agni as it is called in Ayurveda. Your mood, energy, state of mind and your bodily functions are all dependent on the quality and strength of your Agni. A low or malfunctioning Agni results in the formation of toxins or Ama, not just on a physiological level but also on a mental and emotional level. Therefore, strengthening Agni and reducing Ama go hand in hand. One can't reduce the body's toxic load without having a good functioning metabolism. You may revisit the particular section in *Chapter Two* to refresh your memory on the importance of these two key concepts in Ayurveda and how they are linked.

Below are some simple practices and recipes you can take on board to strengthen your Agni and to reduce Ama.

General Benefits of strengthening Agni and reducing Ama:

- improves energy and stamina
- slows down ageing
- strengthens immunity
- brings mental clarity

supports healthy, radiant looking skin

regulates bowel movements

essential for good eyesight

improves nutrient absorption

Sipping Hot Water

Benefits:

flushes toxins out from the body

breaks down food and helps to digest it

along with physical activity supports bowel movement

helps to purify the mind

supports weight loss

reduces food cravings

is helpful in breaking up congestion in chest and sinus region

provides essential hydration to the body

The advantages of sipping hot water throughout the day are endless. It is a cheap but highly effective remedy that has been used in Ayurveda for thousands of years.

Recent research conducted at London South Bank University by Martin Chaplin suggests that the boiling of hot water reduces the amount of hydrogen bonding. Therefore, its molecular mass decreases. Interpreting this from an Ayurvedic perspective, boiling water increases its 'lightness', which means the quality of water becomes more Vata-like. Also the very fact of exposing water to heat adds Pitta to it. Both the quality of lightness and heat are what increase your metabolic fire. So sipping hot water during your main meals and also during the day increases your metabolism and strengthens your Agni.

In the early nineties, I remember ordering hot water in a restaurant in the Black Forest in Germany. The waiter looked at me as if I had come from another planet. It was only when I explained to him that I wanted to have a 'tea without the bag' that he understood what I wanted. In this instance it wasn't a cheap remedy at all; I got charged 5.00 Deutschmark at the time for the exclusivity of my drink. Probably the most expensive 'tea without the bag' I ever drank.

Very often, when being introduced to the concept of 'sipping hot water', clients ask if they can add some lemon juice or freshly sliced ginger to it. Of course, all of these additions are helpful and have a specific health benefit; however, if you start your Ayurvedic journey, just keep it simple and stick to hot water initially. Depending on your metabolic type, variations can be made. For example, if your digestion is 'irregular and cold' or 'underactive and damp' you can add a couple of slices of fresh ginger to the hot water or boil the water with some fresh ginger. Alternatively, a couple of drops of lemon juice can be added. But remember, even without these additions, plain hot water can work wonders for any metabolic type.

Directions:

Boil approximately 1–1½ litres of good quality water for 3–5 minutes. Then keep hot in a thermos flask and sip throughout the day. Alternatively, just have a couple of sips during your main meal.

Important note:

For weight-loss support, sip hot water every fifteen to thirty minutes throughout the day. This improves cellular metabolism and helps in breaking down fat tissue. Here the key is frequency, not quantity; and it has to be hot, similar to tea.

Warm Water with Lemon/Lime Juice and Honey

Benefits:

- kick starts your digestion in the morning
- helps to keep you regular
- balances the pH level
- cleanses the liver
- aids weight loss
- boosts immunity
- helps fighting infections
- increases your energy
- brings mental clarity

Lemon and lime have a similar chemical composition. They have a very high concentration of a compound called 'kaempferolas' as well as the phytochemical called 'limonin'. Both are powerful protective agents against cancer. Further, lemon and lime juice are also known to improve immunity due to their natural antibiotic properties. Although lemon and lime are acidic on their own, once metabolised they are an excellent alkaline food, which is the key to good health and a pre-requisite to losing weight. Also, lemons in particular are high in pectin fibre, which can be helpful in fighting hunger cravings. Lemon and lime help loosening Ama (toxins) in the digestive tract due to their high vitamin and mineral content.

The warm water serves to stimulate the gastrointestinal tract and peristalsis – the waves of muscle contractions within the intestinal walls that keep things moving.

Adding honey to the drink is optional; however, it adds to the cleansing effect of the drink due to its scraping action. If you choose to use honey, it is best to use Manuka honey as it has the so-called 'UMF' (Unique Manuka Factor), which is known as a powerful antibacterial agent not only when touching surfaces, for example when coating the back of the throat, but also throughout the body as a whole.

How to Prepare:

Mix one teaspoon of raw honey, unheated and of good quality (Manuka honey is best), with the juice of two teaspoons of lime or lemon juice in a glass of warm (not boiling) water.

Directions for Use:

Take this remedy as a 'wake-up' drink once in the morning on an empty stomach.

Important note:

If you have an overactive and heated Agni, it is best to replace lemon juice with lime.

Stimulating Ginger Aperitif

Benefits:

- stimulates digestives secretions
- improves appetite
- enhances taste
- reduces possibility of gas and bloating
- picks up your energy instantly
- reduces nausea

If you want to impress your guests then you should consider preparing this stimulating aperitif. The main ingredient of this drink is freshly squeezed ginger juice. Ginger has ample health benefits. Besides its effect on increasing digestion and nutrient absorption, it has a strong anti-inflammatory action. For me, presentation is as important as the actual food or dish itself. Therefore, I encourage you to serve this ginger drink in frosted shot glasses to add to the 'uhhh' and 'ahhh' effect of the drink.

What You Need:

- ginger grater or regular grater
- small bowl
- cheese cloth
- about 5 centimetres (2 inches) of organic, fresh ginger
- organic, cold pressed liquid honey
- lemon juice
- water
- pinch of salt and pepper
- 4 shot glasses, 30millilitres or one fluid ounce each

This recipe makes approximately 120millilitres of ginger drink – suitable for four guests.

How to Prepare:

1. Prepare the shot glasses

- Prepare a powder mix of equal parts of dry ginger and finely grated jaggery (other sweetener such as xylitol or organic brown sugar can also be used).
- Moisten the rim of the shot glasses.
- Dip the glass: turn the glass upside down and dip it in the ginger-jaggery powder mix, as if the glass rim has ink on it and you're trying to stamp a perfect circle in your powder mix.
- Place the shot glasses into the freezer for ten minutes.

2. Prepare the ginger juice

- Wash the ginger root and grate it. If you use non-organic ginger, it is advisable to peel the ginger before grating.
- Squeeze out the ginger juice from the grated pieces into a small bowl using cheesecloth or a fine household strainer.
- Add one tablespoon of good quality, cold-pressed liquid honey and the juice of one lemon (25 millilitres).
- Add approximately equal amounts of water to the freshly pressed ginger juice.
- Add ¼teaspoon of black pepper and ¼ teaspoon of rock salt.
- Use a whisk to blend the ingredients well, until the honey has dissolved.

Get the frosted glasses out of the freezer and pour the juice into the glasses. Serve immediately.

Directions for Use:

Best served fifteen minutes before a main meal. If you don't entertain guests or if you are pressed for time, you can also simply cut a couple of slices of fresh organic ginger, sprinkle a few drops of lemon juice on it, and add a pinch of black pepper and salt. Chew about fifteen minutes before a meal.

Important note:

The amount of ginger juice that you can get very much depends on the quality of the ginger; the fresher the ginger the more juice. You can use a regular household juicer to obtain the juice.

Agni Delight

Benefits:

- helpful in reducing acid reflux
- improves digestion
- helpful in improving appetite
- reduces gas and bloating
- excellent when overeaten
- reduces cravings for sweet

'Agni Delight' is the result of my passion for making Ayurvedic remedies palatable. It is based on a traditional Ayurvedic formula to support digestion and nutrient absorption by combining traditional Ayurvedic methods of medicine preparation, such as pounding and triturating, with the art of creating delicious pralines. Agni Delight is a healthy gingery chocolate treat full of surprises. Its true taste unfolds layer by layer as it melts in your mouth– a real feast for your taste buds.

This is a convenient and effective method of warming Agni and assisting the digestive process, especially in cases of low appetite and whilst travelling when food routines are disrupted. Also, it is excellent if you feel like having a little treat between meals or if you have overindulged.

Direction for Use:

Take one Agni Delight before or after meals as needed. To optimise its effect, Agni Delight is best to be used like lozenges.

Order your jar of Agni Delight by contacting www.ayuwave.com

Metabolic Boosters: Spice Blends to Suit Your Metabolism

Benefits:

- helps improve irregular, overactive and underactive metabolism
- supports weight loss
- reduces symptoms of indigestion such as gas and bloating
- increases mental clarity and energy levels

The metabolic boosting spice blends below are best when prepared fresh. You can grind them by using a pestle and mortar or use an electric spice blender. If you use a spice blender, please be careful not to overheat the spices. Any seeds, such as cumin, fenugreek and fennel can be dry roasted prior to grinding to release their precious essential oils. Be careful not to burn them though. It is best to dry roast them separately. The best way to store the freshly ground spices is in Miron glass jars.

Why Miron Glass?

In ancient Egyptian times, 3000BC, violet glass was used to store valued substances. The colour violet has one of the highest vibrations on the colour spectrum. Miron glass, when held up to the sun or a strong light, has a deep, radiant, violet colour. It is the most effective at preserving important contents, much more so than blue, green, amber, brown or black glass. Most products decay or deteriorate in natural light, especially sunlight, which will accelerate the process of molecular decay in natural compounds. But Miron will block the complete spectrum of visible light with the exception of violet, ultra violet and infra-red light. This unique combination offers optimal protection against the ageing processes that are released by visible light, thus lengthening durability and potency of products. When it comes to spices, they lose their aroma easily; but when stored in Miron glass they maintain their freshness for months. Plus the permanent 'violet life radiation' adds to the potency of the spices.

Metabolic Boosters for:

- Irregular or cold digestion

- ° fennel   3 parts
- ° cumin   3 parts
- ° ajwain   2 parts
- ° dried ginger   2 parts
- ° black pepper   1 part
- ° turmeric   1 part
- ° rock salt   1 part
- ° asafoetida   ½ part

- Overactive or heated digestion

  - ° coriander   3 parts
  - ° fennel   3 parts
  - ° cumin   3 parts
  - ° turmeric   1 part
  - ° rock salt   1 part
  - ° dried ginger   ½ part

- Underactive or damp digestion

  - ° dried ginger   3 parts
  - ° turmeric   3 parts
  - ° black pepper   2 parts
  - ° fenugreek   2 parts
  - ° cumin   1 part
  - ° coriander   1 part
  - ° rock salt   1 part

Directions for Use:

Sprinkle ½–1 teaspoon over your lunch and dinner or have with some warm water fifteen minutes before your main meals. You can also fry the spice blend in a little ghee or oil and pour over cooked dishes or add to soups whilst simmering.

Applying Essential Oils

Benefits:

- helpful in improving digestion
- reduces symptoms of indigestion such as gas and bloating
- can help in relieving constipation
- can be useful in reducing symptoms of pain and cramps
- brings metal clarity

In Ayurveda, each of the five senses is related to one of the elements. The sense of smell is linked to the element of earth, thereby constitutes the grossest of all, which is nevertheless considered an important sense. The sense of smell– the limbic system– is said to be 10–100,000 times more receptive than sight, taste and touch combined. The smell of coffee can take you back into your grandmother's kitchen, with her image vividly flashing in your memory. The environment talks to us through its smells, with precise messages that go beyond the spoken word.

Traditionally, in Ayurveda medicated oils have been used when massaging. Even though they have proven their effectiveness over thousands of years, essential oils are known to be much more potent and stronger than medicated oils.

Records dating back to 4500 BC describe the use of balsamic substances with aromatic properties for religious rituals or medical applications. Egyptians were the first to discover the potential of fragrance.

Essential oils have a similar chemical structure to human cells and tissues. Therefore, they can easily be identified and accepted by the body. They have a unique ability to penetrate the cell membrane and thereby spread throughout the blood and tissues. This is because the molecules of essential oils are very small. For example, when topically applied to the soles of the feet, they can be tasted on the tip of the tongue within minutes.

The quality of essential oils is of utmost importance, particularly when used therapeutically. Oils that are adulterated or of inferior quality will not produce any therapeutic effect; in fact, they can create toxic reactions such as rashes, burning and skin irritations. It is best to use grade 'A' therapeutic essential oils as they are produced according to international standards. Today oils are often extracted under high heat, which is quick, rather than with a low heat and low pressure, which is preferable. In addition, unwanted chemical constituents are added to intensify the aroma and to increase the quantity. These oils present potential dangers for consumers. People might wonder why they do not get the expected benefits and conclude that essential oils do not work.

The use of essential oils in Ayurvedic massage can be extremely effective if the oils are of high quality. They act similar to Ayurvedic herbs. Their energetics produce specific effects on health; however, an extensive study of the energetics of essential oils is necessary to use them safely in an Ayurvedic clinical practice.

Essential oils can be used to create balance on all five elemental bodies; however, the following table suggests a range of oils that can be used to help improve your Agni and thereby your digestion and metabolism, depending on your metabolic type. *

*If you don't know your metabolic type, go to www.NaturalHealthMatrix.com to download your free assessment form or complete the form at the end of this book.

Type of Metabolism	Essential Oils	Suggested Base Oil	Indication
Irregular or Cold	Ginger *Zingiberofficinalis*	Sesame Oil	helpful in reducing pain, indigestion such as gas and flatulence, regulates digestion
	Fennel *Foeniculumvulgare*		relieves cramps and colicky pain, helpful in reducing symptoms of indigestion such as gas, bloating
	Anis *Pimpinellaanisum*		relieves cramps, can be helpful in soothing to a nervous stomach, reduces flatulence

Overactive or Heated	Ginger *Zingiberofficinalis*	Coconut Oil	helpful in reducing pain, indigestion such as gas and flatulence, regulates digestion
	Peppermint *Menthapiperita*		soothes upset stomach, helpful in relaxing muscles thus support relief of gas and bloating
	Coriander *Coriandrumsativum*		reduces excess heat, supports the liver, reduces flatulence
Underactive or Damp	Ginger *Zingiberofficinalis*	Mustard Seed Oil	helpful in reducing pain, indigestion such as gas and flatulence, regulates digestion
	Black Pepper *Pipernigrum*		reduces cramps, relieves pain, warming and stimulates digestion
	Lemongrass *Cymbopogoncitratus*		reduces flatulence, improves digestion, can be used in intestinal infections

Create Your Own Digestive Blend

For general massage purposes, I suggest you use a total of 25 drops of essential oils to 50 millilitres or 1.7 ounces of carrier oil. This is equal to a 2.5% strength.

- For irregular or cold Agni

Formula: anis 5%, ginger 10–15%, fennel 40-80%

Example:

- ° carrier oil: 50 millilitres of sesame oil
- ° anis seed essential oil: 1 drop
- ° ginger essential oil: 4 drops
- ° fennel essential oil: 20 drops

- For overactive or heated Agni

Formula: ginger 5%, peppermint 10–15%, coriander 40–80%

Example:

- ○ carrier oil: 50 millilitres of coconut oil
- ○ ginger essential oil: 1 drop
- ○ peppermint essential oil: 4 drops
- ○ fennel essential oil: 20 drops

- For underactive or damp Agni

Formula: black pepper 5%, ginger 10–15%, lemongrass 40–80%

Example:

- ○ carrier oil: 50 millilitres of mustard seed oil
- ○ black pepper essential oil: 1 drop
- ○ ginger essential oil: 4 drops
- ○ lemongrass essential oil: 20 drops

Procedure:

- Apply the essential oil mix to the lower abdomen and the entire region around the navel.
- To enhance the effect I suggest you apply heat by either using a hot water bottle or a warm, damp towel to the area around your stomach and lower abdomen for approximately five or ten minutes.
- If you don't have any of the above-mentioned essential oils available, you can also do a castor oil pack by applying warm castor oil to the lower abdomen and stomach region. This is excellent to reduce cramps (also menstrual cramps), abdominal pain, gas and bloating. Apply heat by either using a hot water bottle or a warm, damp cloth to the area around your stomach and lower abdomen for approximately five to ten minutes.

Stay Emotionally Calm & Mentally Cool - Connect to Your Higher Self

Your mind, on one hand, can be your biggest asset; on the other hand it may prove to be the greatest monster. Finding ways to control this monster has become more and more a challenge in a world faced with an information explosion from the environment around us, which demands that we attend to many stimuli simultaneously and then determine which to process and which to disregard. This mental overload numbs our senses, resulting in emotional constraints– a life circumstance that becomes increasingly difficult to handle, giving rise to the formation of two new diseases that I would like to call 'Mental Obesity' and 'Emotional Constipation'. These are created by a mind that is overloaded with information that can't be processed, leading to a build-up of mental and emotional toxins, which affect your physical health.

Mental Obesity and Emotional Constipation, according to my view, are the two major causative factors for most diseases of the modern age. Therefore, in my clinical practice with my clients who struggle with their extra pounds, for example, the first step in addressing their weight is not by prescribing a new diet, but by teaching them self-help techniques to deal with their Mental Obesity and Emotional Constipation. Once that is sorted, the physical weight will drop more naturally. These procedures increase self-awareness, which makes you realise how your life is controlled by the ping pong game between the mind and the emotions, where your mind justifies your emotions and your emotions in return feed your mind.

Let's look at the following scenario to understand this concept.

Your partner has commented on the fact that each time you come home and are stressed, instead of exercising you seek comfort by eating chocolate. This comment may upset your feelings. Immediately, your mind seeks justification in saying that you have had such a stressful day at work, needing to face so many challenges; you are too tired to exercise and you deserve that piece of chocolate.

How dare your partner criticise you for your behaviour? Usually you are so good and control your cravings for most of the day. Your emotional body responds to the mind's justification with a greater sense of discomfort, and you start feeling angry. As a result your mind goes on: *But my partner is always pointing the finger at me. I can do what I can, but it is never good enough. All week I don't eat anything that I shouldn't, and just when I have worked so hard, I am made to feel guilty and am being picked on for not exercising.*

Before you know it, you are caught in the ping pong game and your initial feeling of being upset quickly escalates to anger and perhaps rage, which makes you eat more and more of the chocolate, and the idea of exercising disappears as a mirage in your mind.

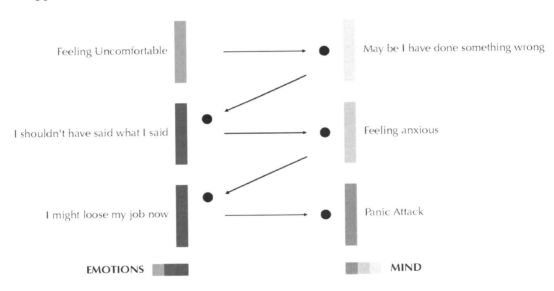

Perhaps it might be useful at this point to revise the section on the 'Mental Body' in the previous chapter, where I discussed in detail how an overloaded and restless mind leads to false brain messages and emotional patterns, which over time form unhealthy habits–how not you but your mind controls your actions. In summary, the key message is that if you wish to turn your health around, you have to find ways to break the cycle of false brain messages, which are the cause of any unwholesome practices.

The OBC Technique

Benefits:

- helpful in changing unwanted habits
- increases self-awareness
- links you with your higher self
- brings mental calm and peace
- stops repetitive thought patterns

Procedure:

Step 1:'O'-Observe

Find a calm and quiet place where you can be undisturbed for some time. Sit upright with your feet placed on the ground and your spine straight. Make sure you are comfortable.

Take a couple of deep breaths in and then breathe slowly out. Breathe in and out through your mouth if possible. Elongate your 'out' breath; perhaps you can count up to four when breathing in and up to six when breathing out. This will give you immediately a sense of calm and peace.

Now observe what is happening emotionally; just screen through your physical and emotional body. Perhaps you may feel worried or you may experience pain. Then, as an example, repeat the following sentence in your mind:

"Here I am [*Name*], observing myself feeling [e.g. *worried*]."

Stop right there and try not to engage in the natural tendency of the mind as it tries to seek justification as to why you experience what you experience. This might be challenging initially, but it will get easier as you practise. Just repeat the sentence above in your mind, for some time until you start feeling a sense of relief and ease.

The aim is not to engage in the mind and the ping pong game, which seems to be the natural tendency. This is like training a new muscle; just keep practising until you have mastered it. What you will feel is immediate relief as you distance yourself from your emotions. Remember you are not the emotion and you are not what your mind wants to tell you. You can choose where you focus your attention so that your actions align with your higher self. The key is not to stop those feelings such as anger, frustration and so on from arising, but to learn how to work around them by accepting that they are there. This is how you can control them, and by controlling them you have then the ability to focus your attention on things that matter to you, on what you and your true self wish to achieve.

This is the first step to stop the ping pong game and to take control over your mind and emotions, which is the pre-requisite for both of the other two steps. Please don't move on until you have mastered this step, otherwise you will set yourself up for failure.

Step 2:'B'–Be

Now that you have practised Step 1 for some time, I would like to ask you to find ways of getting yourself in a state of 'being', where you get in touch with your higher self. To do this, please close your eyes and try to recollect memories where you had that door between your individual self and your higher self open. This can be accomplished by thinking of a loved one, remembering a particular place you have been to or by imagining a specific event in your life.

Once you have found that key to open the door between your individual- and higher-self, focus on that sensation of contentment, happiness and fulfilment. Keep 'milking' the experience. Once you feel the emotion has reached its peak, I would like you to lock that emotion into your subconscious by 'tapping it into your forearm', using the index and middle finger of your left hand. Imagine that you are depositing this life-supporting emotion into your 'happiness' account.

As a task, over a minimum of one week, whenever you walk around and get that sense of fulfilment or contentment – perhaps when walking through the park, when watching children at play, when listening to a specific piece of music, anything that triggers this emotion – remember to lock it into your forearm, and keep adding it to your emotional 'happiness' account.

Over time you build up your happiness account, and by locking that experience into your subconscious, any time you feel your have lost that connection to your higher self, by tapping onto your forearm you will be able to unlock that memory and restore your sense of emotional balance quickly.

Step 3: 'C'–Create

Only when you have mastered Step 1 and Step 2, move on to Step 3. When you are able to recognise how you feel and change your emotional state by allowing yourself to access your higher self, you are now in a position to create what you wish to create. You will have created that neutral space where you are able to change that initial feeling of worry, into a sense of trust, for example.

If you miss Step 1 or 2, then your subconscious will defer from your conscious. This is why, from my perspective, positive thinking doesn't work. This would be like pretending that the sun shines when it rains. First, you have to accept that it rains. Then, by changing your negative feeling about the rain into a sense of peace and ease, you are able to create the sunshine. Remember, this is just a metaphor; it might not be that easy to change the weather, especially here in London.

Important note:

- **Pittas**–please don't think you can master all the steps at once. Take one step at a time. Remember, less is more.
- **Vatas**– don't get bored with the practise. Only move on once you have mastered each step, otherwise you set yourself up for failure.
- **Kaphas**– endurance is the key. Don't give up and keep in mind once you have mastered the technique, it will be there with you for the rest of your life if you so wish.

Directions for Application:

The 'OBC' technique can either be practised on a regular basis at home in a calm and quiet place or you can use it in your daily life. For example, when you are at work in a meeting and you start feeling upset about a comment you colleague has made, just breathe and practise: "Here I am [*Name*] observing myself feeling [*upset*]". Nobody will notice your secret, but as a result you will start taking control you your life again, rather than having life (your mind and emotions) control you.

Mantra Meditation

Benefits:

- increases self-awareness
- provides direct access to heightened awareness, thereby activating your body's own inner self-repair mechanism
- relaxes and calms the mind
- enhances intelligence and improves memory
- reduces emotional stress such as fear, anxiety, anger
- balances all five bodies simultaneously
- develops the whole brain
- brings inner peace and happiness
- provides stress relief and enhances creativity
- improves relationships
- slows down the ageing process
- reduces blood pressure, improves quality of sleep, reduces risk for cardiovascular diseases, depression, ADHD, addictions, etc.

Reflecting back, I know I wouldn't be where I am today without my mediation. It helped me to transform from a grey caterpillar into a colourful butterfly, able to spread his wings and take off. It allowed me to say goodbye to a shy, introverted young teenage boy, who had the confidence of a rabbit when facing a fox; not because someone told me what to do, but because I went within and listened until a deep inner knowing guided me to that Matrix. And by walking through, the door to heightened awareness opened up for me. For the first time, at the age of nineteen, I was allowed to gain a glimpse of what heightened awareness truly means.

My family struggled understandably with this transformation. They thought seeing a priest and undergoing a kind of exorcism would work and sort me out. Well it didn't. With great determination, perhaps even some stubbornness, I did what I felt was right for me at the time. Today, meditation provides that safety net that makes me relax when performing life's thrilling trapeze act up high in the air. I know I am safe, and when I need a break I can just let go of the swinging bar knowing that the net below will catch me.

Perhaps, to put it in less dramatic language, life without my regular meditation practice would be like having a cappuccino without the sprinkle of chocolate or starting the day without having brushed my teeth.

Long gone are the times when meditation was considered something religious or sect-like. A lot has changed for the good. In 1989, shortly after the Berlin Wall had come down, I was invited to move to East Germany for a short period of time to start teaching Ayurveda and meditation. One evening, I organised a talk in one of the community centres. And when I arrived at the venue to pick up the key I was told that the event had been cancelled. "Cancelled by whom? I am the organiser."

The next day, when I saw the papers, I had an inkling of what was going on and who was behind the silent attack. I always dreamed of making headlines in a newspaper, and there I was– a huge picture of me on the front page of a major paper. "Witches, gurus, ghosts, teachers of Ayurveda and meditation. This is what you can get: internal bleedings, mental disorders and sexual addictions".

What a blessing that there is science and twenty-five years have passed. Today, more than 500 research papers have been conducted and published in major journals around the world that confirm the benefits of meditation on all areas of life. One of today's leading identities in brain research and meditation is Dr Fred Travis. He has published around forty studies in peer-reviewed journals on the benefits of meditation.

As discussed in the very first chapter of this book, your perception is shaped by the state of your mind. In one of his talks, Dr Travis mentions that the brain is the interface between the inner and outer. The quality of your brain function influences what you hear or see, which in turn will determine your response. He compares your ever-changing brain with a river, which cuts into a valley that flows down the hill. Similarly, life's experiences are like streams of electrical activity that leave a mark on your brain. If the experience is life-supporting and positive, it encourages higher integrated functioning of the brain. Negative or traumatic experiences, however, leave a scar or dysfunctional mark on the brain. This activates the fear centre of your brain, which alters your experience of the world. You become vulnerable and perhaps people see you as someone who can't be trusted or that is useless, because this is what their brain tells them. As a consequence, this fear centre in their brain turns on the 'fight and flight' response, which in turn switches off the front part of the brain responsible for seeing the bigger picture that allows them to put things in perspective.

If traumatic experiences have turned the fear centre on, experiences of the opposite of a trauma are needed to turn it off again; experiences that are holistic and not fragmented' experiences that are silent and not chaotic. Meditation does achieve that, but there are different types of meditations that have to be chosen thoughtfully.

Some meditation techniques such as concentration practices used by Tibetan Buddhists or loving kindness meditations– where the mind is kept on one thing and you don't let the mind move– have a high level of cognitive control. When your brain waves are measured in that state, an EEG indicates gamma waves, which are the fastest brain waves with the highest level of cognitive control, of twenty to fifty cycles per second.

A medium level of control would be the so-called theta waves, which go up and down between five to eight times per second. In this case, you let things go through your mind but you don't control them, so the brain frequency is lower. Practising 'mindfulness' where you simply observe what goes on in your mind is an example.

Meditation practices in both of the above categories keep the mind active in the process of thinking and doing, similar to when the fear centre of the brain is turned on. What is reported by Dr. Travis is that these meditations have very minimal effects because of their limitations in reducing post-traumatic stress disorder.

However, the last category of meditation is what is called 'autonomic self-transcending', which has the lowest level of cognitive control. These are meditations that transcend their own activity and allow you to transcend thinking and experience the essence of who you are. They take you from the state of self-awareness to a heightened state of awareness. These practices have to be automatic and effortless, since any interference or actions will not allow for this process to happen. Mantra meditations such as Transcendental Meditation fall under this category.

Research has shown that during Transcendental Meditation, for example, the front of the brain is more alive and the subcortical areas are less operational.

This indicates that the integrative system is more active and thereby able to take any experience and put it into a whole, or in other words, into perspective. The hyper-vigilant part of the brain, the back, becomes quieter.

What's happening when transcending is that you are now resetting your mind and body, it takes you beyond thinking to silence, where those fear signals from the brain are turned off. Your integrative centre is then able to see the bigger picture and your exaggerated part of the brain settles down.

The key to this experience is the use of a 'mantra' or sound. The very word 'mantra' is derived from Sanskrit, meaning to 'free the mind'. A mantra is a sound that has a specific energetic vibration or frequency, just like an instrument or any other sound. There are certain sounds when listened to that resonate with you and others, perhaps extremely high or low pitched ones, that to make you feel uncomfortable. Mantras can be extremely powerful when chosen correctly and are right for you. It is for this reason that I suggest you learn a mantra from a specially trained teacher.

If the mantra is in line with your vibration, it becomes like a tuning folk that aligns all your five bodies simultaneously. Your thoughts, your emotions and your physiological functions vibrate in tune with the vibration of the mantra, producing the desired effect, even without you needing to know its meaning. For example, take the Sanskrit word 'Akasha', which you might remember from one of the previous chapters. Just simply by repeating the word 'Akasha' for a while, and if practiced effortlessly, your whole being will resonate with its meaning, which is 'space' and you will have the experience of expansion and space.

Mantras can be used to neutralise the effect of any negative thoughts, emotions or other experiences stored in the cells. Therefore, I believe anyone who seriously embarks on the journey to health and wellbeing should practise mantra meditation on a daily basis to support the healing process and to activate their own inner self-repair mechanism. Remember *your body knows best*. You just need to provide the space where this knowing and remembering can happen. Mantra meditation becomes the Matrix that takes you to that place.

There are several Sanskrit 'seed mantras' which have no literal translation, but have been used for thousands of years, with certain effects due to their particular vibrational qualities. What enhances very much the effectiveness of any given mantra is the intention of the person giving the mantra; but even more importantly is the intention of the person who practices the mantra. In my clinical practice I use medical astrology to choose very specific mantras that can be helpful depending on my clients' health needs.

Below I have suggested **five seed sounds that correspond to each of the five elemental bodies.** Those seed sounds can be used safely for **re-alignment**. I have also suggested a mantra that can be used to improve **digestion and metabolism**.

Shreem: the seed sound to balance the 'earth body', which supports harmonious interactions of all organs and organ systems and their corresponding physiological functions.

Hreem: the seed sound to balance the 'water body', which brings emotional balance and enhances the experience of joy and love.

Kleem: the seed sound to balance the 'fire body', which improves energy and supports change.

Dhleem: the seed sound to balance the 'air body', which creates mental peace and contentment.

Pleem:the seed sound to balance the 'space body', which is the link to your higher awareness.

Om Agnidevaya Namaha: a mantra to improve digestion and metabolism, which supports detoxification and weight loss.

How to Practise Mantra Meditation

- Sit upright in a comfortable position with your eyes closed.
- Ensure that you are not disturbed by switching off your phone and informing your family or flat mates.
- After a few seconds of sitting quietly, start repeating the mantra in your mind.
- Repeating the mantra should not be a clear pronunciation but rather like a faint idea in the back of your mind.
- Don't concentrate on the mantra; allow the nature of the sound to do its job.

- Don't aim at erasing your thoughts. If thoughts arise, just come back to the mantra.
- Repeat the mantra effortlessly until its vibration becomes part of you.
- Trust the vibration of the mantra to calm the mind; imagine the mantra being the vehicle that takes you to that place of quiet and calm.
- Practise for a minimum of fifteen to twenty minutes, ideally in the early hours of the morning and later in the afternoon on an empty stomach.
- When you finish with the mantra, stay seated with closed eyes for at least two to three minutes before opening your eyes.

Important note:

- Should you find it difficult to stay seated with closed eyes for fifteen to twenty minutes, start with five minutes and slowly build up to the ideal time.
- If mantra meditation seems impossible to do then please practise the 'OBC' technique for a while before moving on to the mantra meditation.
- The 'Agni Mantra' can be practised when preparing food or in a quiet space fifteen to twenty minutes before your main meal, twice daily as described above.

Elemental Mudras

Benefits:

enhances the experience of heightened awareness

increases self-awareness

deepens any meditation practice

brings energy and emotional balance

balances respective elemental body

You probably noticed, especially when you injure yourself or when trying to extract a splinter from the tip of your fingers, how sensitive they are. The fingertips are a concentration of nerve endings, which can be seen as free energy discharge points. These energies can be made visible through Kirlian photography, for example. By touching together these fingertips or by bringing them in contact with specific parts of the palm of your hand, you redirect this 'Pranic' life force back into your body, back to the brain, along specific energy pathways or subtle channels. By applying tension or pressure to those specific points using a specific 'mudra', neural circuits are being formed and the redirected energy recharges the cells of your inner organs and organ systems.

This can be compared to acupuncture, where needles are being used to create electrical impulses in the body. The advantage in mudras is that the pressure to be applied on the nerves is automatic and controlled by the shape and size of the fingers and not by external agencies.

Depending on which mudra you use, you balance different aspects of your being, working on the different elemental bodies. The mudras explained below are specifically to harmonise their respective elemental body and can be used as another Matrix to enhance any healing process and to encourage self-repair, especially when practised alongside the mantra meditation.

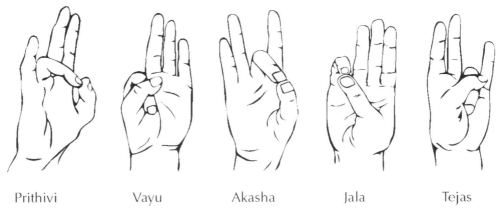

| Prithivi | Vayu | Akasha | Jala | Tejas |

Akasha Mudra

- balances the space body
- activates self-repair mechanism
- connects with heightened awareness

How to do:

Press the tip of your thumb and middle finger together and extend your index, ring and little finger.

Vayu Mudra

- balances the air body
- brings peace of mind
- may help to balance the nervous system

How to do:

Connect your index finger to the base of your thumb and use the thumb to press down the index finger. Let the other fingers be straight.

Tejas Mudra

- balances the fire body
- increases your energy
- may support metabolism, digestion, and detoxification

How to do:

Fold the ring finger at the base of thumb and press it with the thumb at the second phalange. Keep the rest of the three fingers straight.

Jula Mudra

- balances the water body
- balances your emotions
- may help to maintain water balance, elimination and cleansing within the body

How to do:

Joining the little fingertip with the tip of the thumb, keep the rest of the three fingers straight. Make sure you do not press the tip of the little finger near the nail as it causes dehydration rather than moisturising

Prithivi Mudra

- balances the earth body
- may help to improve physical weakness
- increases patience and tolerance

How to do:

Join the tip of ring finger and thumb whilst keeping other three relaxed and extended.

Important note:

All mudras are ideally performed in sitting position 2–3 times a day for 15–20 minutes to observe their benefits; either on their own, depending on which of the five elemental bodies you choose to work on, or alongside a mantra meditation.

Yoga

Benefits:

- improves cardiovascular health and hormonal functions, lymphatic circulation, fat reduction, muscle tone, bone and reproductive health
- reduces stress and anxiety
- useful in balancing blood pressure
- enhances digestion and removes toxins
- improves organ function e.g. kidneys, pancreas, lungs, intestines
- improves circulation and supports weight loss
- increases oxygen uptake
- abates negative emotions such as depression, anger, greed
- balances all five bodies simultaneously

Ensuring harmonious interaction in your daily life can be challenging if you needs to make conscious choices all the time. A powerful method when built into your everyday life that programmes your ability to re-align with your body's inner self-healing mechanism is yoga. The term 'yoga' means 'harmonious interaction'; therefore, Ayurveda simply borrows yoga's philosophy and practices to guide one's lifestyle. Doing yoga once, twice or even three times a week is not yoga. You have to embrace the spirit of it on a daily basis. Breath control, meditation and specific bodily postures are used to enhance wellbeing and to encourage repair. Aiming at restoring health through Ayurveda without its sister science yoga would be like running a car without fuelling its engine.

Breathing Practices

Benefits:

- cleanses and harmonises all five bodies simultaneously
- develops the lungs
- improves immunity
- supports digestion and nutrient assimilation
- helps to control mind and emotions
- brings mental clarity and increases energy
- improves strength, courage and enthusiasm
- balances the flow of Prana

In yoga, there are very specific breathing practices that enhance the flow of Prana, the vital force that permeates everything in creation and is essential for healthy living. These practices help to connect your awareness with the five elemental bodies, where blockages can be released, resulting in improved wellbeing and an active self-repair mechanism.

Alternate Nostril Breathing to Balance Vata

Place the index and middle finger of your right hand in between your eyebrows. Use your right thumb to close your right nostril. Breathe out through your left nostril. Breathe in using your left nostril, close the left nostril with your ring finger, release the thumb and breathe out of the right nostril. Then breathe in through the right, close the right with your thumb and release your ring finger to breathe out through the left nostril. Repeat this process slowly and with full awareness for 5–10 minutes daily. This practice is extremely effective to calm the mind and balance an overactive Vata.

Cooling Breath to Balance Pitta

Sit comfortably, either on a chair or on the floor, with your shoulders relaxed and your spine naturally erect. Slightly lower your chin, curl your tongue lengthwise and project it out of your mouth to a comfortable distance. Inhale gently through the 'straw' formed by your curled tongue as you slowly lift your chin toward the ceiling, lifting only as far as the neck is comfortable. At the end of the inhalation, with your chin comfortably raised, retract the tongue and close the mouth. Exhale slowly through the nostrils as you gently lower your chin back to a neutral position. Repeat for 8–12 breaths. This very much balances an overheated Pitta.

Breath of Fire to Balance Kapha

Place your thumbs in the palms of your hands and form fists. With your fingers pointing away from you, place your fists in front of your shoulders. Take a deep breath in. As you forcefully inhale, throw your arms up into a full vertical stretch, spreading your fingers as wide as possible. As you forcefully exhale, pull your hands back into fists in front of your shoulders; imagine pulling a curtain in front of your eyes. Repeat this movement twenty times continuously. Do three rounds of this with a gap of a few seconds in between. This energises the body and activates the mind. It breaks a stagnant state of Kapha.

General note for all breathing practices:

- Sit comfortably in an upright position with your spine straight.
- Relax your face and head.
- Chin should be parallel to the floor and head, neck and spine in line.
- Slightly roll your shoulders back to open up your chest.
- Increase the duration of your practice gradually.
- Ideally practise after yoga postures and before meditation, or use as a stand-alone practice.
- Best to practice on an empty stomach.

Yantra – Protection from Harmful Energetic Fields

Benefits:

- helpful in protecting against electro-magnetic fields
- balances your energies, thus supports wellbeing
- brings mental peace and emotional calm
- assists in deepening your meditation experience
- increases self-awareness
- balances the flow of Prana
- connects all the five elemental bodies

You may be able to choose your food carefully, to decide when to go to bed and if you exercise or not; but what is beyond your control is the exposure to high levels of electromagnetic fields. Wherever you go, there is Wi-Fi radiation from computers, mobile phones, television screens and any other electronic device. You are bombarded constantly with these modern-day electronic vampires, whether outside your home, in the home or at work. One way to protect oneself from such radiation is with a 'Yantra'.

A 'Yantra', in particular the 'Sri Yantra', is one of the most ancient symbols formed by nine interlocking triangles that surround and radiate out from a central point. Various research scientists have shown interest in this ancient Vedic Yantra. The American physicist Dr Patrick Flanagan calls the Sri Yantra the 'king of power diagrams' and describes its energetic effect as seventy times greater than that of a pyramid construction. The particular Yantra I recommend is made of copper and has been found to be helpful in protecting against radiation and electro-magnetic influences when tested using the Bio Meridian system.

Besides being helpful in protecting against electromagnetic influences, a Sri Yantra made of copper can also be helpful in safeguarding your own energy. There are those people who are extremely sparky by nature, who electrify you by their presence and therefore are a pleasure to be around. On the other hand, there are those who leave you drained even after the shortest interaction, be it in person or on the phone. They may leave feeling uplifted and better, but you feel like a fish left out of the water for too long. I always carry a small version of the Sri Yantra in my pocket, especially when doing treatments, to protect me and to keep me charged. Here is a testimonial of one of my clients, which I think speaks for itself.

"My mum bought me the Yantra and that night I put it under my pillow. I was woken up a couple of times in the night, which for me is very unusual, as I could hear something vibrating and wasn't sure what it was. I then realised when I took it out from under my pillow, the vibration stopped. And as soon as I put it under my pillow and put my head down I could hear it again! So I put it beside my bed.

I now carry it around with me everywhere I go in my handbag and have found it amazing in helping to protect my energy when working with my clients. I am a trained Pilates teacher and do a lot of rehabilitation and healing work. On Thursdays and Fridays I have very long days and usually feel quite energetically drained by the end of it. The first day I had my Yantra I put it on the side where I was working, and just glanced at it at various times throughout the day when I felt I was with clients who particularly drained my energy, I just connected with it and felt life force come into me (I know that probably sounds a bit weird!). I now keep it in my handbag and just connect with it whenever I feel I need to. I have found I don't feel drained any more, and my clients who sucked me dry no longer do. But I still feel I have given the same amount of myself to them but just with a little more self-protection.

It really is amazing. Who would have thought that a square bit of metal could do that!!

Amanda, 28 years, Pilates Teacher

Order your Sri Yantra by contacting www.ayuwave.com

Find Your Own Natural Rhythm

There are alarm clocks that go off, deadlines that have to be met, buses to catch and appointments to follow. The ticking of the clock dictates life on a daily basis and I don't suggest you stop paying attention to it. However, the purpose of this section is to help you find a natural rhythm in your life, where you become aware of the ticking clock but don't allow it to take over. You may ask, "How can this be possible?" Well, by simply understanding the difference between rhythm and routine.

A routine is a strict, rigid approach to a day's scheduled events, which may make you feel like you are failing when you have missed one aspect or fallen behind. On the contrary, a rhythm is a much friendlier notion, which keeps order but also allows for flexibility, movement and fluidity. Rhythm moves you. You dance to it, find your style, allowing you to let go a little so you can enjoy the moment and see where it takes you. Routine? Not so much. You march to a routine. It's a steady metronome keeping time. And if you sway, if you linger, if you move out of order or fail to complete a step, then you fail. You're out of time. You're lagging behind.

Well begun is half done.

Take some time and sit down with a piece of paper after you have read through this section of the book. Work out your ideal morning routine by starting with small steps; incorporate perhaps one or two aspects of the following suggestions. Include those aspects you think are essential, such as having breakfast or emptying bowels; the important ones and the 'nice to haves'. Bring them into a sequence that you think would work for you, ensuring you have added one or two or perhaps three aspects of an Ayurvedic regime depending on your availability of time. Over the next few days, bring those aspects into your life and let your day unfold around it.

Once this has become second nature, you may add or change the order of some of these aspects. Let the rhythm swing with the motion of the day, speed up the tempo when needed and slow it down when you can. Be kind to yourself and enjoy the process as each day unfolds like a new play on the stage of life where you are its director.

Daily Oil Massage

Benefits:

- lubricates muscles, tissues and joints
- increases flexibility
- promotes youthfulness
- eliminates accumulated toxins
- increases softness and lustre of skin
- increases self-awareness
- improves energy – flow of Prana
- creates emotional balance

The skin is the largest organ of our body. No matter if covered in moles and freckles, black or white, silky or dry, flawless or blemished, the skin is a living organism that wraps around our inner core like silk surrounding a cocoon. Cuts and wounds vanish in a miraculous way just as drawings in the sand are swept away by the silent winds of time. With every cycle of the moon, dead skin has been replaced, revealing a totally new layer of skin enabling us to leave the past behind.

Our skin is much more than just decorative; it is the largest organ in the human body. The average adult is covered in approximately 1.7 square metres of skin, weighing approximately 11kilograms. On average there are fifty touch receptors for every square centimetre of skin, giving a total of five million sensory cells overall. The skin forms a protective shield, separating the outside world in which we live from the inner realm of our bodies and consciousness.

From an Ayurvedic perspective, the skin is the sense organ of touch, related to Vata, the element of air. Vata plays an important role in all sensory perception. For example when the cool sea breeze touches the hair of our skin, the neurons in the skin are activated. These produce signals that travel via specific nerve fibres to the spinal column and from there to an area of the brain called the somatosensory cortex, where the cold breeze is recognised. It is Vata that initiates all movement and communicates from cell to cell; it is also Vata that moves the other Doshas. The Ayurvedic massage, in particular a synchronised massage, balances Vata, therefore improving sensory perception. The sense of touch in massage evokes vibrations in the form of chemical messengers, conveyed through sensitive nerve pathways, which can produce a healing effect such as naturally occurring antidepressants, anti-cancer and anti-aging substances as well as hormones that enhance circulation.

The psychologist Harry Harlow conducted a ground-breaking research on touch at the University of Wisconsin in 1958. Baby monkeys were taken away from their mothers and put into metal cages. They were given various objects as a source of comfort and security. The monkeys preferred cuddling with a soft cloth rather than with a wiry object that had a face and offered nourishment. This research suggests cuddling and tactile stimulation can often be more important than food.

Tiffany Field, PhD, founder of the Touch Research Institute, University of Miami School of Medicine, initiated a research when her daughter was born prematurely in 1982. This showed that infants given pacifiers during their tube feedings, gained more weight and came off tube feeding earlier, leading to an earlier discharge.

It appears that in the modern world we are denied one of the most natural instincts – touch. The elderly are sometimes only touched when performing hospital procedures. Touch is as vital as the air we breathe. It provides comfort when we are in despair. A gentle pat on the back can be a source of comfort when we feel unwell. A genuine hug can help more than a thousand words. Caring touch is the medium to convey love and nurturing, and massage is the tool to address this deficiency, as it supports harmony and healing.

There are various ways as to how an Ayurvedic massage can be performed. It can either be done on a daily basis as a self-practice or by one or two therapists. Having a fourhanded massage done on a daily basis might be a luxury, but it is definitely something worth experiencing at some stage during your Ayurvedic journey, especially if the massage is done with equal pressure and in perfect synchrony.

What distinguishes Ayurvedic massage from other types of massages is the use of warm oil, preferably sesame oil, and its rhythmical movements. The warm sesame oil wraps like a cloak around you, a symbol of security, giving you protection and comfort. This then creates a sense of *I am all that there is...* It provides a direct pathway to the Matrix, opening the door for healing and repair.

The perfectly synchronised rhythmical movements of the massage strokes create a sense of unity and provide deep rest and relaxation. As the massage progresses, you experience a sense of oneness where you might not be able to differentiate one stroke from another. This evokes a sense of peace. The inability of the mind to distinguish between one or many, right or left, up or down, provides the right space for you to let go. Stress can be released and harmful experiences of the past can be removed.

The warm sesame oil forms a layer that protects both the client and practitioner, just as embryonic fluid shields the unborn baby. Even though the process of letting go can be a rough journey, if the client is able to let go, it can be like an ocean of bliss. The viscous, soft and sweet nature of oil purifies and acts like a safety net, supporting you through the process in a graceful manner. The rejuvenating experience of massage provides the necessary support and fertile ground for new seeds of wellness to grow. Effective reprogramming of past cellular memory can now take place. Like a phoenix emerging from the ashes, you leave with a subtle sense of youth and wellbeing. With the key to preserving wellbeing in hand, like painting on a white crisp canvas, the desirable traits now come alive.

Ayurveda uses sesame oil as the base oil for most body therapies. Thousands of years ago, the classical textbooks of Ayurveda considered sesame oil as one of best mediums for massage. From an Ayurvedic perspective, sesame oil has a high mineral content and is heavy and heating in its qualities, thereby reducing Vata and Kapha. It is known to promote healthy growth of hair, heals wounds and is good for the skin, teeth and gums.

In an American study conducted by the University of Miami in 2000, full-term six-week- old healthy infants were massaged with different oils, including sesame. The results showed a significant improvement in growth on babies who were massaged with sesame oil.

In summary, if you don't have the means to experience a four-handed massage or even a single person massage, daily oil massage is still an absolute necessity if you embark on the Ayurvedic journey to enhance wellbeing. It can be incorporated easily in your daily rhythm and once you get into it, you wouldn't miss it; just like you wouldn't leave your home without having had a shower in the morning.

Procedure

Unless prescribed differently, use organic, good quality cold pressed sesame oil or oil that is Dosha-specific and suitable to your constitution .As an alternative, olive or coconut oil can also be used if sesame oil is unsuitable.

Massage oil ideally should be cured by heating it to about 108°C. Most of the ready-made Ayurvedic massage oils are cured already; however, if not, here is how you can do it. Pour the oil in a saucepan and add a drop of water to the oil. Heat the oil until the proper temperature has been reached. An indication of this when the water had evaporated and produces sound. Be aware that oils are flammable and therefore should be cured as follows:

- Always heat oil on low heat, never on high heat.
- Oil should never be heated unattended.
- Once the oil reaches proper temperature, it should be removed from heat immediately and stored in a safe place to gradually cool down.
- Place back into a bottle, ideally a Miron glass bottle, once the oil has cooled down and use as you go.

Before starting the massage, the oil should be at or slightly above body temperature; therefore, pour some oil into a stainless steel cup and warm the oil up by placing the stainless steel cup into a bowl of hot water. Alternatively, you can get a small glass bottle that can be put into a 'baby warmer'.

Massaging the head

- Place a small amount of oil on your fingertips and the palms of your hands.
- Begin to massage your scalp.
- Use comfortably soft pressure.
- Massaging of the head and entire body should be done with the palms of your hands rather than with the fingertips alone.
- Spend proportionately more time on massaging your head than on other parts of the body as the head is one of the most important parts to

be emphasised during Ayurveda oil massage. It is the control unit that regulates and navigates the operation 'human body' in its entire complexity.

Face massage

- Apply oil gently to your face and the outer parts of your ears.
- Massage your face staring on forehead, temples, cheekbones, cheeks, nose, above upper lip and chin. There is no need to apply much pressure to these areas.
- Massage the front and back of your neck and the upper part of the spine.
- Continue to use the palm of your hands in a rubbing type of motion.

Then you may apply a small amount of oil to your entire body and proceed with the self-massage to each area of the body. This will allow maximum of time for the oil to stay on the body and to get absorbed through the skin.

Massage upper body

- Massage your arms next.
- The suggested movement is back and forth over your long bones and circular strokes over your joints.
- Massage both arms including hands and fingers.
- If you haven't applied oil already, spread some warm oil to your chest and abdomen.
- Massage in gentle, circular motions over your abdominal region, following the bowel in a clockwise manner.
- Then massage the back and your spine as far as you can reach and as far as is comfortable for you.

Massage lower body

- Apply similar strokes to your legs like you have used for your arms: back and forth motion over long bones, circles on joints.
- Lastly massage the soles of your feet.
- Don't forget your toes and the region in between your toes.
- Spend proportionately more time on your feet than on other parts of body, as the feet are especially important.

- Always aim to use the palm of your hands.
- Massage vigorously back and forth over the soles of your feet.

Important note:

If you want to get the best benefit of your daily oil massage, please ensure that you don't take a Vata approach by rushing through the process. If you are pressed for time, it is better to concentrate on some parts of your body such as head and feet, and massage them with full attention, rather than doing the whole body in a hurry. Remember, one of the main purposes of this treatment is to increase self-awareness. In my clinic some of my clients find it extremely difficult to self-massage. If that is the case for you, start by massaging your feet or your hands and slowly build up towards a full body massage over a period of time.

The whole self-practice can take between 10–15 minutes and it is recommended to have a warm shower or bath after the massage. Many times I am asked the question as to whether it is better to leave the oil on the skin for a period of time. There are many different views depending on which book you read; however, I suggest to my clients to wash the oil off after approximately twenty minutes. Twenty minutes allows plenty of time for the oil to penetrate through the skin and to loosen up the toxins. Some of these toxins come back out through the skin; therefore, if you leave the oil on for too long, it blocks the pores of your skin and prevents your skin from breathing.

Please use a natural shower gel without any nasty chemicals and don't apply any additional moisturiser afterwards. If your system is very dry, you may find that the oil gets soaked up as soon as it is applied. This is a sign that your body is extremely dry. Please be patient and resist the temptation to apply anything after your shower or bath. It may take a couple of weeks until the deeper layers of your skin get saturated with the oil, especially if your system is very dry.

Silk Glove Massage

Benefits:

- increases energy levels
- exfoliates the skin
- detoxifies
- promotes lymphatic drainage
- increases circulation to all the tissues
- helps in weight management
- useful to prevent and reduce cellulite

Ayurvedic silk gloves made of raw silk and are used for Ayurvedic skin brushing. You can use them on yourself or a massage client. This Ayurvedic massage is an exfoliation and detoxifying technique that consists of dry lymphatic brushing with raw silk gloves. This enhances circulation and releases static electricity that supports lymphatic flow according to Ayurveda. Silk glove massage can be helpful in weight management, prevention and reduction of cellulite.

Directions

It is best to do the massage before your bath or shower in the morning. Garshana takes approximately 3–5 minutes to perform. All strokes are vigorous and should be done with full attention to increase self-awareness. Always massage towards the heart. To optimise the effect, use your whole hand when massaging. With time you may increase the speed and number of strokes for maximum stimulation and cleansing.

You can apply circular strokes on the joints, for example, shoulders, elbows, wrists, hips, knees, ankles and long strokes on the limbs. Please use gentle pressure on your face, neck and heart.

- Start with your face and neck: massage back and forth across the forehead with circles on the temples and cheeks. Massage back and forth using the thumb or index finger of both hands along the sides of the nose. Then move back and forth across the chin and use circular strokes upwards on the front of the neck. Finish with up-and-down movements on the back of the neck using your fingers.

- Remember always to massage towards the heart. For women, start by massaging your left arm; for men, start with the right arm. Begin your massage with up-and-down movements on the top of your hand, followed by circles on the palms of your hand. Also, include the spaces between each finger. Use a circular motion on the wrist and back and forth strokes on the forearm, covering all surfaces. Continue with circles on the elbow, then move up the upper arm with back and forth strokes, covering all surfaces until you reach the shoulder.
- Repeat the sequence on the opposite arm.
- Massage your shoulder joint with circular strokes and keep reaching towards your upper back as well as you can. Then apply circular strokes in the lower back region and move up and down your back as far as is comfortable for you.
- Massage the upper chest area with back and forth movements in a V-shape towards the heart to cover the lymphatic area.
- Massage the abdomen using horizontal strokes, with hands moving across the stomach region in opposite directions. Then with both hands moving in a diagonal direction towards the groin, which is the second lymph location. Continue with both hands, moving in a diagonal upward movement toward the ribs, then up and down the sides of the chest.
- Continue your massage by working on the legs. Massage back and forth on the feet, emphasising the soles of the feet and the spaces between each toe. Using both hands, apply circles on the ankles. Move up and down the calves and up and down the lower leg, covering all surfaces. Then apply circles on your knee with both hands and keep moving up the thigh with up-and-down movements, covering the whole of the upper leg. Finally, massage the hip and the buttocks with circular movements. Repeat on the opposite side. For women, start on your left leg, and for men, begin your massage on the right leg.

Important note:

Please use less pressure when massaging the face and neck. Also, if you have sensitive skin, use less pressure and reduce the speed. A slight reddening of the skin after brushing is normal and indicates increased circulation.

You can order your high-quality burette silk Garshan gloves from *Ayuwave*. Just go to www.ayuwave.com

Ionised Water in a Copper Cup

Benefits:

- cleanses colon
- helps regulate elimination
- helps maintain body's pH levels
- energises the water
- eliminates toxic elements and free radicals
- prevents ageing
- helps fight undesirable viruses and bacteria

First recognised in the 1870s as a normal constituent of blood, copper is a trace mineral that plays an important role in our metabolism, largely because it allows many critical enzymes to function properly. Copper plays an important part in iron utilisation and the elimination of free radicals. It is also responsible for the development of strong bone and connective tissue and a healthy formation of melanin, which protects various organs such as eyes and ears, as well as the skin.

Copper reacts with water and ionises it, as can be ascertained by its pH measurement. That is the reason micro-organisms get killed in such water. Copper has been proven to kill bacteria due to what is called the 'oligodynamic' effect. The 'oligodynamic' effect was discovered in 1893 by Swiss researcher KW Nägeli as a toxic effect of metalions on living cells, algae, moulds, spores, fungi, viruses and microorganisms, even in relatively low concentrations. This antimicrobial effect is shown by ions of various metals such as gold, silver, copper and iron. Certain metals such as copper are known to be far more poisonous to bacteria than others for example, stainless steel or zinc.

If you want to live long and stay healthy, keep your water in copper utensils.

Directions For Use

Keep a cup of water in a copper vessel for 8 –10 hours overnight. It is best to cover the drink and consume first thing in the morning at room temperature.

Important note:

It is recommended not to drink copper cup water during pregnancy and if you have already high levels of copper.

Tongue Scraping

Benefits:

- helps in reducing bad breath
- removes bacteria
- improves taste
- increases self-awareness
- cleanses and stimulates your organs
- boosts immunity
- prevents toxins being reabsorbed back into your body
- improves digestion by activating saliva production and kindling your Agni

The surface of the tongue is a breeding ground for bacteria that can cause infection in teeth and gums and is often responsible for bad breath. A research paper published in the *Journal of the American Dental Association* in 1996, reports that in approximately 80–95% of cases, bad breath originates in the oral cavity, mainly from material on the rear of the tongue. Tongue scraping is known to reduce bacteria and bad breath by up to 75%.Thus, when incorporated in your daily routine, tongue scraping can be far more effective in combating bad breath than a mouthwash or tooth brushing.

In Ayurveda, different areas of the tongue are connected to our internal organs. Regular tongue scraping stimulates the reflex zones of your internal organs, which has a beneficial effect on their functions. By removing the coating on your tongue you open its pores, thereby enhancing your taste buds. Without proper removal ofmucus, taste buds can become blocked and this can inhibit your sense of taste.

Tongue scraping is a good way to increase self-awareness and can be a great assessment tool. So get to know it. Just like your skin, looking at your tongue can tell you a lot about your health. The daily practice of cleaning your tongue with awareness, by analysing what comes off it, can put you in direct contact with this assessment tool. For me, this is an important point since I can observe on a day-to-day basis if there are any significant changes. Perhaps I may discover which foods eaten the previous day may not have been agreeable. If the coating of the tongue is more whitish and thick, this indicates toxins due to accumulated Kapha. If the coating is more yellowish or greenish, this is linked to Pitta. Sometimes the coating can be light brown in colour, which indicates impaired Vata.

The *Ayuwave* tongue scrapers are made of pure silver. By using a silver tongue scraper regularly, micro-particles of silver are being released into the bloodstream, which is an excellent way to improve immunity and to support health and wellbeing.

The first time I ever engaged in tongue scraping convinced me, and I knew there was no going back. Tongue scraping first thing in the morning is like a wake-up call to my organs, asking them to get active. It is something that can be incorporated so easily in your daily routine. It is a must when you embark on your Ayurvedic journey.

Directions For Use

Grab the two ends of the tongue scraper and reach the arch of it to the back of your tongue. Scrape firmly forward several times. Rinse the tongue scraper between each scrape. Make sure you wash off all the bacteria and saliva that's collected on the scraper. You should scrape your tongue at least two to three times per cleaning. Wash your tongue scraper thoroughly in hot water, dry and put away.

You can order your silver tongue scraper from *Ayuwave*. Just go to www.ayuwave.com

Oil Pulling and Gargling With Sesame Oil

Benefits:

- detoxifies
- brightens your teeth
- helpful in healing bleeding and/or receding gums
- prevention and treatment of halitosis (bad breath)
- useful in treating oral infections
- prevents tooth decay and gum diseases
- reduces inflammation and increases immunity
- can be helpful in treating many systemic conditions throughout the body

Ayurveda had seen and discussed the benefits of using oil orally in its classical scriptures 2,000 years ago, long before its recent 'new discovery' in the West. I find it interesting that something that has been around for thousands of years all of a sudden becomes a useful but fashionable accessory to some who claim to have discovered the latest and newest solution to many health problems. In fact, I have to take a deep breath to stay cool and not allow 'the wind to spark my fire'.

Did you know that there are more bacteria in your mouth than people living on this planet? The pockets around your teeth provide a breeding ground for many bacteria, viruses, fungi and parasites and their respective toxins, which could easily be tested through a saliva test. These unwanted microorganisms have the potential to thrive and multiply, and they can easily migrate throughout the rest of your body. Just think about how many times a day you swallow your saliva and how easy it is for these microorganisms to spread throughout your body. Not only that, these harmful microorganisms produce further toxins as a simple by-product of their very existence that cannot be destroyed by stomach acids or easily be neutralised by your body's immunity.

Many of these unwanted microorganisms don't even pass through the intestinal tract but get absorbed sublingually through the capillaries of your mouth, directly into your bloodstream. Imagine you are hooked up to an IV that is directly feeding low levels of poison into your system twenty-four hours a day, seven days a week, affecting your immunity.

This perhaps can be seen as the bigger problem since your immune system needs to fight these troublemakers constantly. If your immune system becomes overloaded or burdened by excessive stress, poor diet or environmental toxins, these organisms can spread easily throughout the body, causing further problems that may lead to inflammation, infections or other health risks.

Oil pulling is one of the most remarkable methods of detoxification and healing known today. It is a very simple, harmless, cost effective yet powerful therapeutic technique that activates certain enzymes that help draw out the toxins in your mouth. Oil is used as a medium to cleanse and detox; it 'pulls' out bacteria and other debris. In his book *Oil Pulling Therapy*, Dr Bruce Five compares this process with an engine. The oil acts like a cleaner that picks up any dirt and grime, and when drained expels this debris with it. As a result, the engine runs smoother and lasts longer. Similarly, when you eliminate these harmful toxins from your system, which could potentially be the culprit for many other health problems such as heart disease, arthritis or diabetes, you remove the cause for many systemic diseases and therefore will experience improved health and wellbeing.

In summary, the health benefits of oil pulling have been widely researched in many countries worldwide. According to the *African Journal of Microbiology Research*, oil pulling is an effective defence against the bacteria associated with dental caries (tooth decay).Also in 1996, *Andhra Jyoti*, an Indian newspaper, conducted a survey among its readers on the effects of oil pulling, where 89% reported its healing abilities. The analysis indicated cure of the following types of chronic diseases: pains in the body and problems pertaining to the neck and above; allergy and respiratory problems of the lungs like asthma and bronchitis; skin problems like pigmentation, itching, scars, black patches and eczema; diseases of the digestive system; arthritis and joint pains; heart disease; blood pressure and diabetes; hormonal disorders; even cancer and AIDS.

Directions:

For maintenance purposes, oil pulling is best done in the morning on an empty stomach. However, if you have any particular health issues it can be done up to three times daily, three to four hours after a meal.

Take one tablespoon of cold-pressed, organic sesame oil into your mouth. At the beginning of this process, whilst the oil is still clean, gargle for a few seconds. Next move the oil slowly in the mouth; then begin rinsing, swishing and pulling the oil through the teeth without swallowing it. Practise this for at least 15–20minutes. You'll find that the oil will start to get watery as your saliva mixes with it. Keep swishing.

If your jaw muscles get sore whilst swishing, you're putting too much effort into it. Relax your jaw muscles and use your tongue to help move the liquid around the inside of your mouth. When you do this correctly, you'll feel very comfortable.

If you have the unbearable urge to swallow and if it becomes too unpleasant, spit it out and try again. It can be a bit unpleasant at first when you're not used to it, but soon it will become second nature, like having a shower or brushing your teeth. Twenty minutes will allow enough time for the oil to become more watery and whitish in colour, which is an indication that the process is completed.

As the end of the oil pulling session approaches, spit the oil out then rinse the mouth with warm salt water. Salt water rinsing isn't absolutely necessary but is very helpful as an antimicrobial and to soothe any inflammation. It has also proven to be effective in rinsing out any toxins that may be left in the mouth.

Suggested Order of Daily Oral Hygiene Regime:

- Get up and scrape your tongue.
- Have a glass of water to stimulate saliva and to hydrate the oral cavity. This also helps to normalise pH levels.
- Do the oil swishing for 15–20 minutes.
- Rinse your mouth with warm water or salt water.
- Massage your gums with your finger.
- Brush your teeth using toothpaste free of fluoride and harmful chemicals such as propylene glycol and sodium laurel sulphate.

Important note:

- **Never swallow the oil** because it is loaded with bacteria and unwanted toxins.
- Although today many oils are recommended, the best oil is still sesame

oil. *Sesamumindicum* is considered to be the queen of oil seed crops because of its beneficiary effects on health.

- Spit the oil into a garbage bin, not the sink, as it can solidify in the drain.

Have a Good Night's Sleep – Don't Miss the Angel Train

Benefits:

- improves your quality of life
- promotes youthfulness and slows down ageing
- improves your energy
- brings mental calm and emotional balance
- increases your immunity
- ensures a healthy digestion
- supports the body's natural rhythm to cleanse and detox
- reduces the risk of common diseases such as obesity, diabetes, high blood pressure, premature aging, depression, anxiety and other psychological disorders.

... there are times in my life when I wake up sighing before the alarm goes off only to realise that I have not yet fallen asleep, where a healthy sleep has almost become a luxury, especially when travelling and in emotionally stressful situations, such as deadlines that need to be met or when being confronted with a terminal illness of a loved one. In my practice I have seen clients whose need to sleep has almost become a burden and is seen as waste of time.

Apologies if I repeat myself, but again we have to blame the Vata society for this, where speed has become the driving force of life. Just the thought of uncompleted projects could become the very cause of insomnia, a typical phenomenon in times of Ethernet and tabloids.

Lack of sleep does not only deprive us of quality of life, but it can also be the start of many serious diseases. In Ayurveda, sleep is known as one of the three pillars of good health that provide the foundation for physical, mental and emotional wellbeing.

How Do We Define Sleep?

A healthy, restful sleep means that you fall asleep easily when you switch off the light and sleep peacefully. The goal is to sleep deeply for six to eight hours without the help of medication. You should wake up rested and refreshed.

A good night's sleep is crucial for your health because this is the time where important hormones are being produced, such as human growth hormone (HGH). HGH is responsible for the immune system; it regulates fat metabolism, supports muscle growth and generally acts against ageing. This hormone is produced the most during the deep sleep phase.

Sleep has its own rhythm, which repeats itself about every ninety minutes. Immediately after you fall asleep, a phase begins where your sleep is light, which then slowly turns into the deep sleep phase. Then an REM (rapid eye movement) phase occurs and this is the time of the night when you start dreaming. This REM phase is initially short but extends through the night. This means as the REM phase extends, your time of deep sleep reduces. During a six-hour sleep, the average time of deep sleep is only two hours.

We usually have three to five periods of REM phase during a night's sleep. These phases occur at intervals of one to two hours and are highly variable in length. An episode of REM sleep may take five minutes or an hour. Most people spend 25% of their sleep dreaming and the rest in a state of non-dreaming.

Sleep Stages Through The Night

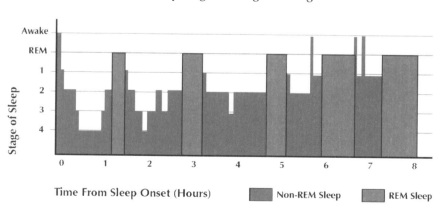

199

Sleep Disturbances According to Ayurveda

- Difficulty falling asleep is caused by a Vata imbalance– excess of the element of air. This could be due to irregular lifestyle, night shift, excess worry or thinking.
- Intermittent awakening is caused by a Pitta imbalance, linked to the element of fire, perhaps due to frustration, anger, excess heat or an over acidic body.
- Excessive sleeping, but still waking up in the morning feeling un-refreshed is caused by an imbalance of Kapha, related to the element of earth. This could be caused because of overeating, lack of exercise, depression or toxicity.

What Happens If We Do Not Get Enough Sleep?

Studies have shown that if you wake up around three o'clock in the morning, during the following twenty-four hours your immune system is weakened and you are more susceptible to viruses and other pathogens.

 Research has also shown that lack of sleep increases the production of inflammatory chemicals (cytokines). Lack of sleep can also lead to the production of chemicals, which can be causative factors for the development of obesity and diabetes. Diseases such as high blood pressure, premature aging, depression, anxiety and other psychological disorders may be the result of sleep deprivation.

When considering sleep from an Ayurvedic perspective, unhealthy sleep leads to the reduction of Ojas or(immunity), the vital nectar of life which is extracted from food. Ojas, as the end product of all digestive processes is responsible for enhanced energy, enthusiasm, joy, clear thinking, and balanced communication between mind and heart.

General Suggestions for a Good Night's Sleep

- Follow nature's sleeping pattern and go to bed around 10pm. The best quality sleep is the one you get before midnight. My grandmother, although she had never heard the word Ayurveda in her life, always used to say to me, "Hurry up, Thomas. If you wish to catch the last train of the angels, you have to be in bed before 10pm".

- Make sure your bedroom is ready for a good night's sleep: avoid any clutter, too many books and keep your bedroom clean and at a comfortable temperature, free from work-related material.

- Reduce electromagnetic field radiation (EMF) by removing your computer, TV, mobile phone or any other tabloid from your bedroom. There have been many books written on the health risks of EMF.

- Avoid having a heavy meal just before you go to bed. Remember, it takes between three to six hours for a meal to be digested.

- Avoid stimulating and spicy foods at night time.

- Massage your lower extremities, especially your feet, with warm sesame oil (Vata and Kapha), ghee or coconut oil (Pitta).

- Have a brief walk in fresh air for approximately twenty minutes after your dinner.

- A warm bath or shower can help to calm the nervous system and relax the body.

- Avoid watching any aggravating or stimulating movies prior to going to bed since whatever is in your mind prior to going to sleep will occupy you during the night.

- Try to avoid having a heavy discussion or argument prior to bedtime.

- Improve the quality of sleep along with gentle relaxation and breathing exercises, yoga and meditation practice.

- Have a comforting bedtime drink suitable to your constitution. See specific recipes below. Alternatively you can order the ready-prepared *Ayuwave* night drink at www.ayuwave.com.

Helpful Tips Specific to Your Constitution

Vata – difficulties falling asleep

The problem is insomnia itself increases Vata, the bio-energy responsible for proper circulation and movement. Its light and mobile qualities make it difficult for the mind to rest. Any irregularity increases Vata and this creates a vicious circle. Vata prevents you from falling asleep; whilst not being able to get a good quality sleep increases Vata itself. So the cause and the effect are the same and often lead to neurological stress. When a Vata individual falls asleep eventually, many times the sleep is light and restless, never quite reaching a deep sound sleep. There is a tendency for waking up in the early hours of the morning, between 2 am and 4am, and not being able to go back to sleep.

In this case, a regular daily routine is important: going to bed at the same time, waking up at the same time, regular meal times. All this is essential to balance Vata. Also, food should be mainly hot, well cooked and plentiful. Placing a hot water bottle on your stomach can be relaxing. Avoid stimulants such as coffee and alcohol, which can disrupt natural sleep cycles.

Have your **Vata night drink:**

Boil half a cup of organic, good quality cow's milk or almond milk for 3–5 minutes with half a cup of water. Add the following spices: nutmeg, ginger, saffron, poppy seeds. You can add some jaggery for sweetener if needed.

Pitta – intermittent awakening

If you fall into the Pitta category of sleep, you usually tend to lose sleep between 10pm and 2am, as this is the time that is naturally ruled by Pitta. If you find it difficult to fall asleep before 10pm, this could be because of Pitta's intense sharpness of intellect combined with the quality of lightness from Pitta's fire, which may make this a tempting time to 'burn the midnight oil'. If this is the case then you might also be prone to indulge in midnight snacks, which can further impair your quality of sleep and digestion. Pittas can also have a difficult time letting go of stress from the day and relaxing before bed.

An overactive Pitta needs cooling, so make sure that the bedroom is cool and not too hot. Use cotton sheets, keep the bedroom dark and read inspirational literature for a few minutes before bedtime. Write down your thoughts and concerns before falling asleep; this 'downloading' soothes a raging spirit.

Have your **Pitta night drink:**

Boil half a cup of organic, good quality goat's or coconut milk for 3–5 minutes with half a cup of water. Add the following spices: coriander, cardamom, ginger, saffron and fennel. You can add some coconut palm sugar for sweetener if needed.

Kapha – excessive sleep

A Kapha constitution may have the problem of sleeping too much. Some people believe they need nine, ten or more hours of sleep. In the morning, these people often still wake up feeling heavy and tired and show symptoms of sleep deprivation. They may yawn all day and still have the need for an afternoon nap.

In this case, the solution would be to look at your diet. Make sure you only have a light meal such as soup at night time. The best is to eat around 6pm. Avoid sweets, dairy, pasta and other grains. Drink hot ginger tea throughout the day. This helps to reduce food cravings and increases your digestion. Avoid napping during the day and get up in the morning before sunrise.

Have your **Kapha night drink**:

Boil half a cup of organic, good quality cow's milk or almond milk for 3–5 minutes with half a cup of water. Add the following spices: ginger, turmeric, black pepper, cumin and clove. You can add some honey for sweetener if needed.

Important note:

In summary, sleep deprivation is often not taken seriously enough and the much-quoted 'beauty sleep' can be a simple but effective recipe for improved health and wellbeing. Finding a healthy sleeping routine should become an important aspect of your daily routine, as sleep is your best health insurance.

Regular Exercise

Benefits:

- supports weight loss
- improves self-esteem
- enhances a good quality sleep
- regulates digestion
- stimulates lymphatic flow, thereby eliminating toxic waste
- increases energy
- lowers the risk of many chronic diseases such as stroke, diabetes, heart disease, osteoarthritis

Exercise has always been a challenging aspect of my life. Throughout school, from primary through to senior and junior high school, I struggled with my weight. In fact, I was bullied at school because of my inability to move. I had excellent scores in mathematics, accountancy, languages, religion and, of course, behaviour. But when it came to sports, my scores were on the lower end of the scale. I absolutely dreaded any sporting event at school. I remember one incident where we practised box jumping in class. I used all my strength and courage and ran as fast as I could down the runway, approaching a pile of stacked up boxes three-quarters the height of my body. With full force and a total weight of 88kilograms at the age of fifteen, I jumped onto the take-off board and bang... The shrill laughter of my classmates brought me back to my senses rather quickly and I found myself lying on the floor, with a pile of boxes on top of me. The deadly-white face of my teacher was staring at me and reaching out, struggling to help me up. She was probably more shocked than me.

Soon after, I decided to do something about my weight and the rest is history...However, even after I lost about twenty kilograms in a relatively short period of time, exercise still didn't come naturally to me. That was until I went to drama school. For the first time in my life, I could not wait to go to the dance studio at 7am, two hours before class started, to do my exercises and warm up. I didn't mind the aches and pains, bruises and broken toes, because I absolutely loved what I was doing. I was at the peak of my physical fitness at the age of thirty-five. Today, I need a personal trainer to get me out of bed three times a week at 6 am to keep up my exercise routine.

Perhaps you have asked yourself the question as to why some people succeed at following a regular exercise routine and why others don't. The answer to that is simple. Those who are able to stick to their fitness routine have found a programme that suits them – a mind, body and soul workout.

This is what happened to me. When you match your workout with who you truly are, you enjoy what you do and it is easy to stay active and to maintain your fitness. You will not only see the benefits on a physical level, such as improved cardiovascular health, but also mentally. It distracts and relaxes you for a while, and you start to forget the problems and pressures of your daily life. On top of that, an ideal Ayurvedic exercise routine, following your mind-body type where you love what you do, brings you joy and fulfilment, which will have an impact on your personal as well as social life.

As you know, Ayurveda gives us a model to look at each individual as a combination of the five elements of space, air, fire, water and earth, which then form the three Ayurvedic metabolic types called Vata, Pitta and Kapha. Each of us is born with a certain mind-body type that affects our physical, mental and emotional makeup. The secret to discovering an exercise programme you will enjoy and stick to is to match your total makeup to it. But how do you find your mind-body type? First, you must take a personal inventory. Think of your body frame, natural pace, energy level and personality traits.

Here are some suggestions how you can find your ideal exercise routine based on your metabolic type:

Vata – Space and Air – Fast and Dry

You need variety in your fitness routines.

Those of a predominantly Vata metabolic type usually have a thin, light frame and excellent agility. Their energy comes in bursts and they are likely to experience sudden bouts of fatigue. Vatas generally are naturally slender from their nervous energy and tend to always be on the move. Vatas often have trouble gaining weight, a sign of their fast metabolism and irregular eating habits. Vatas typically have dry skin and hair and cold hands and feet. They are creative, quick and lively in their actions and thoughts. They sleep lightly and their digestion can be sensitive. When Vata becomes imbalanced, it can manifest as anxiety and nervousness.

For Vata, the key to exercise is variety: go dancing, try a tennis game or Pilates one week. Then do golf, yoga or biking the next. Ideal exercise options to balance Vata should incorporate slow movements, not be too tiring, and help settle the mind and body. Slow dancing, low impact aerobics, tai chi, badminton, walking and yoga are examples of Vata-balancing exercise activities. Although Vatas do best with exercises that are less intense and more gentle, they can take up and train for a marathon or half-marathon if they are able to follow a routine and maintain a rhythm of regular practice, where they slowly build up to peak performance to achieve a set goal.

Pitta – Fire and Water – Heat and Intensity

Try water sports.

A Pitta body type is usually of medium size and weight, often with reddish hair and complexion. They have a warm body temperature. Often they gain muscle mass more easily. They are strong in thought and actions and are ambitious. They may be moderate sleepers and prefer cooler climates. They have good concentration levels and are good leaders. Pittas have strong appetites and digestion. They can be pushy when stressed. Team sports are great, but watch your competitive stress level.

For Pittas it is essential to release heat from your body. Remember, you have the element of fire in you. Water sports are great for releasing this heat. Water, ice or snow-based activities such as swimming, downhill skiing, rowing, surfing and water-skiing are great for releasing this heat. Walking or jogging in a cool shady area, tennis and yoga are also good Pitta-balancing options.

Pittas tend to like competitive sports. They might overdo exercising and they need to watch for balancing it with fun exercise. Also, it is good to remember that Pittas tend to shorten their muscles through weight training, but need to lengthen them through yoga or Pilates. They may, though, find it less challenging and therefore less enjoyable.

Kapha – Water and Earth – Calm and Steady

Use your strength and endurance.

Kapha types usually have a stronger build and have excellent stamina, as well as a strong digestive system. Large, soft eyes, smooth, radiant skin and thick hair are also important Kapha characteristics. Often their sleep is deep and long. They have difficulties in learning, but once learned, they hardly forget. Kaphas are loving and warm-hearted. They have the tendency to gain weight easily and to become lazy and lethargic when stressed.

For Kaphas, running, lifting weights, rowing, swimming, aerobics and hatha yoga are ideal. Activities to balance Kapha should draw on the strength and endurance power of the Kapha individual but also seek to stimulate and generate intensity and liveliness such as through distance walking or running, basketball, racquetball, football and aerobics. Kaphas tend to do well in company. So they should join walking groups, cycling groups, boot camp and even play contact sports.

Exercising is different from physical activity and one needs to perform moderate to intense physical activity most days of the week in order to keep the Agni sharp, detoxification happening and elimination efficient. As you age, your Agni and metabolism start to dwindle, and having a regular intense workout is a way to keep the Agni strong and to maintain a healthy metabolism. In this sense, Ayurveda sees exercise as a form of detoxification. Therefore, not exercising at all can lead to the accumulation of toxins in mind and body. On the other hand, over-exercising could lead to inflammation and therefore toxicity.

Mamsa tissue, or pure muscle mass, is metabolically active and consequently is a form of permanent detoxification. But an excess of Meda, or adipose tissue, can lead to toxicity. Following an exercise regime that supports building of Mamsa tissue is helpful when trying to lose fat, but only in conjunction with a healthy lifestyle and by considering balanced nutrition.

In summary, when it comes to exercise, balance should be the magic word and the key to success is to find a workout routine that matches your Ayurvedic body type. Then exercise no longer becomes a struggle and you'll feel inspired. You will enjoy and stick to your programme whilst reaping the benefits in every aspect of your life.

Important note:

- Dr John Douillard, Ayurvedic doctor and sports coach, recommends exercising within the 'effortless' zone, meaning that you exercise until your heart rate increases and you start sweating. Gradually, this helps you to reach peak performance irrespective of your age and physical condition, without straining and depleting your body. If you want to find out more about his approach, I recommend you read his book *Mind, Body and Sport.*

- If you lack self-motivation, find yourself an exercise buddy who can encourage you to stay active.

- Exercise is best done in the morning. According to your circadian rhythm, between 6 am and 10 am.
- Exercise itself can be a significant physiological stressor, especially if you do heavy workouts. Therefore, your post-exercise nutritional regime should include appropriate supplementation, plenty of rest and water, and most importantly wholesome foods with lots of protein and fresh green leafy vegetables.

Follow a Balanced Diet

At the beginning of this section, I wish to mention that this book is **not** a book on Ayurvedic. It is beyond the scope of this practice-oriented book to go in depth into the elaboration comprehensive understanding of food from an Ayurvedic perspective; this will be my next project. Also, in fact, there is no such thing as Ayurvedic nutrition. Even though the classical texts of Ayurveda discuss a set of principles, nowhere is there a detailed list of Vata, Pitta or Kapha diets. These 'Doshic' diets don't exist, but some form of them have become another fashionable accessory over the past thirty years that sells well.

The aim of this section of the book is to consider some of the Ayurvedic concepts of food in a modern context. I won't go into the 'what to eat' and 'what not to eat' discussion, since healthy nutrition is very personalised and as such highly different from person to person, depending on their metabolic type and bio-individuality. The best way to find out what suits you is through a personal Ayurvedic assessment. The *Ayuwave* approach to nutrition is evidence based and a specific blood test is used in determining food sensitivities; not on an 'energetic' level but by observing how the actual cells respond to food triggers making the test highly accurate.

In Ayurveda it is understood that your body and its diseases are the product of the food you eat. On one hand, food nourishes the body, but on the other hand the body is only an instrument in fulfilling the experience of your higher self. Thus, Ayurveda emphasises nutrition as an essential aspect of the maintenance and promotion of wellbeing. It keeps all five elemental bodies alive and healthy. In fact, the way you feel today is because of what you have eaten approximately forty days ago; this is how long it takes from the moment your food reaches the stomach until it's been fully processed and transformed into its finest components.

Ayurveda does not consider the nutritional value of food in isolation. So it's not so much about carbohydrates, fats or proteins; it rather considers the nourishment food can bring about in an individual. It is important to differentiate between nutrition and nourishment. Nourishment means it does something good for people collectively such as when eating in a community or when sharing food. An article published in the *Canadian Journal of Public Health* by Payette and Shatenstein in 2005 confirms that social isolation has a negative impact on food intake, especially amongst seniors

When it comes to collective eating and sharing food, India is the best example. One of those moments that have stayed with me until today is the memory of my involvement in feeding a group of 4,000 children in an orphanage in Mysore, India. The food was simple, with rice, dhal and vegetables. Perhaps from a modern nutritional perspective, it was of low nutritional value; but what was remarkable was the enjoyment it brought to the children. Looking into their eyes and seeing the smiles on their faces made my heart melt like butter in the sun. This is when food truly became the best possible nourishment.

Every day, when you open the paper or read through most magazines, there is a new diet. You can drown easily in the ocean of diets these days, but in the end there is no diet, only nourishment. Food is nourishment, influenced by your eating habits and the way you prepare your food, which may vary based on how you define life, based on your values. Ayurveda helps to identify values that define the concept of nourishment. It is about developing an attitude towards food.

Nourishment is not as mechanical as a computer, where you simply press a button and you get a printout. You can have the best paint, but you can't put it straight on the wall; you have to prepare the wall first. The more thorough the preparation process, the longer lasting the paint will be and the better the colour will reflect off the wall. It is a process that is very much influenced by several factors such as the nature of food, method of preparation, food combination, quantity, quality, time of consumption and the food consumer's state of mind. And all of these impacts on the ultimate effect the food has on the individual.

Statistics by 'CREDS' (Central Region Eating Disorder Service in New Zealand) reveals that worldwide:

- The failure rate for diets is 95–98%, with up to 90% of dieters putting on their weight again in a short period of time.
- Thirty years ago the average model was 8% thinner than the average woman. Today the average model is 23 % thinner.
- One in four teenage girls may suffer from the symptoms of an eating disorder.

In the USA, Canada and Australia, one in every hundred females has anorexia nervosa and three in every hundred females has bulimia nervosa. In New Zealand, a study was done that found that 80% of females were within normal weight limits, but only 18% of them thought their weight was normal. In Canada, 80% of females have issues with food and their body; half of the entire UK population has problems relating to negative body image. In 2010, just over a quarter of adults in the UK were classified as obese with an estimate that by 2030 half of the UK population will be obese. Dieting is a $33 billion industry in the United States and an over £10 billion pound industry in the UK.

The statistics and findings above are alarming, indicating a world with a disturbed relationship to food. Eating disorders, which are nothing but a mixture of emotions trapped in a body cage, are on the rise globally. When asked "Where do vegetables come from?" many children nowadays answer all too often "From the supermarket". As a society we have lost our connection to food.

Ayurveda asks you to look at your own relationship to food. Does cooking mean you are merely feeding yourself or the family? I say "No". Preparing food is a process for which one has to mentally prepare. Look at food, not so much as a biological process or that it provides nutrients to your body, but as an experience that increases self-awareness. It is not only about eating more of this and less of that; you have to look at your connection to food in relation to what is happening in your life.

Mindful Eating Practices

Benefits:

- increases self-awareness
- prevents overeating
- supports weight loss
- improves digestion and absorption
- brings mental clarity and increases energy
- prevents the formation of toxins or Ama

General:

- Eat in a quiet and relaxed atmosphere, without being stressed emotionally or whilst having an argument.
- Ideally, lunch should be your main meal since digestion is highest around lunchtime, and dinner should be lighter.
- Sitting down whilst eating will support optimal digestion.
- Chew your food well.
- Your stomach likes to be on a schedule, so eat at regular times of the day. Skipping meals slows down your cellular metabolism and may increase weight.
- If possible, go for a brief walk after your main meals.
- Aim to eat only when feeling hungry; allow three to six hours in between meals depending on your metabolic type.
- Give your digestive system a break by planning regular 'liquid days' – see suggestions below.

Food Combining:

- Avoid cold drinks when eating; have some sips of hot water instead.
- Eat natural, single ingredient foods such as vegetables, grains and meats. This means avoiding processed foods with artificial colours, flavours and preservatives.
- Get used to reading labels when shopping. Rule of thumb: the less the number of ingredients the better the product.

- Avoid overeating. Eating lots of starchy foods such as pasta, potatoes and bread can easily make you eat too much.
- If you have fruits, take them away from your main meal.
- If you have a regular cup of coffee, adding cardamom helps in neutralising the acid-forming effect of coffee.
- If you use grains in your cooking, get a mill and grind the grains freshly as you need them. Grains, even when organic, have been sitting on the shelves for a substantial amount of time and are therefore prone to becoming rancid and to have fungus, which often is the cause of gluten/wheat intolerances, not the grain itself.
- If you tend to suffer from gas or bloating, especially when consuming pulses and lentils, I suggest you add black cumin and asafoetida (also known as 'hing') to your dish.

Type of Foods:

- Be spice-wise: why use ketchup and readymade sauces when there is a world of spices out there (see below for further tips on spicing).
- If you like salads, have them at lunchtime preferably, and by adding a sprinkle of lemon juice and some fresh ginger you make them more digestible.
- Include a sensible mix of various types of foods in your diet, such as plenty of vegetables, protein and some grains, so that you are getting the nutrition your body needs.
- It's not about avoiding fats and carbohydrates, especially when aiming at losing weight, but rather that when you have a high carbohydrate meal, you avoid high fat and vice versa. For example, having pasta with cheese is best to be avoided, but having cheese with your meat and vegetables with little to no grains, might be perfectly fine.
- Prepare your food fresh on a daily basis.

If You Suffer From Indigestion or Possible Food Intolerances:

Practise self-awareness by listening to your own needs. If you think you have food intolerances, I suggest you keep a diary and write down what you have eaten, when, and the effect it has on your body and mind. If you are not sure what causes the problem, use the 'elimination' process by cutting out one item at a time, evaluating and then re-introducing. For example, if your dish contains salad, fish and potatoes, cut out the potatoes and see if it makes any difference. If not, re-introduce the potatoes but leave the salad.

Also, sometimes it is about when to eat rather than what to eat. So try to eat different dishes at different times of the day. For example, if you are used to having salad at dinner and you feel any signs of indigestion, try to have the salad at lunch time and see if it makes any difference. Also keep in mind adding certain spices to food can help to neutralise its possible adverse effects (see section on spices below).

Important Note:

Ayurveda does not encourage you to avoid the foods that you may be intolerant to for the rest of your life, but rather helps you to strengthen your digestion so they can be reintroduced at a certain stage without causing any adverse reactions.

Ban Your Microwave

Benefits:

- prevents formation of toxins
- improves healthy formation of all the bodily tissues
- enhances nutrient absorption
- increases your energy
- brings mental clarity and improves memory
- reduces the risk of cancer and other chronic illnesses

These days, microwave ovens can be found in almost every household. They are a very convenient way of preparing food, especially in our Vata society where time is never enough. But how high is the price we pay for this convenience? There is a lot of controversy around this issue fuelled by the growing market of microwavable instant meals. Apart from the scientific evidence, the everyday user should use their common sense in making their own judgements.

How Does a Microwave Oven Work?

Microwave ovens contain a magnetron tube, which causes an electron beam to move electrons back and forth at a very high frequency, producing microwave radiation. In other words, the polarity of the electron changes from positive to negative more than one million times per second. This happens at a frequency of 2.45 gigahertz.

Within one microwave, the rotation of the polar molecules causes friction, which in turn generates heat. The food bombarded with this heat inside the microwave processes at a very high speed. Because this happens on a molecular level the cooking action occurs from the inside of the food to the outside. This reverses the natural cooking process where heat enters gradually from the outside.

Another interesting source of evidence is 'Kirlian photography'. The visual appearance of microwaved foods in Kirlian photography gives a graphic illustration of their diminished state. In comparison to un-microwaved foods these photos show an almost complete loss of colour, detail and radiance, which represents their loss of Prana or life-force. It is evident in these photos that all nutritional value has been destroyed by microwaving.

Ten Reasons to Discard Microwave Ovens

A summary of the results from research conducted in Switzerland, Russia and Germany on microwave ovens and their effects can be found in the book *The Hidden Hazards of Microwave Cooking* by Wayne Anthony and Newell Laurence. Here is a summary of their findings:

1. Continually eating food processed from a microwave oven causes long-term, permanent brain damage by 'shorting out' electrical impulses in the brain (de-polarising or de-magnetising the brain tissue).
2. The human body cannot metabolise (break down) the unknown by-products created in microwaved food.
3. Male and female hormone production is shut down and/or altered by continually eating microwaved foods.
4. The effects of microwaved food by-products are residual (long term, permanent) within the human body.

5. Minerals, vitamins and nutrients of all microwaved food are reduced or altered so that the human body gets little or no benefit, or the human body absorbs altered compounds that cannot be broken down.

6. The minerals in vegetables are altered into cancerous free radicals when cooked in microwave ovens.

7. Microwaved foods cause stomach and intestinal cancerous growths (tumours). This may explain the rapidly increased rate of colon cancer in America.

8. The prolonged eating of microwaved foods causes cancerous cells to increase in human blood.

9. Continual ingestion of microwaved food causes immune system deficiencies through lymph gland and blood serum alterations.

10. Eating microwaved food causes loss of memory, concentration, emotional instability and a decrease of intelligence.

Keep Your Body Alkaline

Benefits:

- makes your skin more elastic and youthful
- promotes a deeper and more restful sleep
- improves immunity
- prevents many chronic diseases
- increases energy and overall wellbeing
- increases mental alertness and improves memory
- improves your skin
- slows down the ageing process
- prevents fungus and malnutrition

The American Journal of Clinical Nutrition recently published a study conducted at the University of California, San Francisco, on 9,000 women over a period of seven years. This study showed that those who have chronic acidosis, when the bodily fluids contain too much acid, are at greater risk for bone loss than those who have normal pH levels. Many of the hip fractures among middle-aged women are connected to high acidity caused by a diet rich in animal foods and low in vegetables.

Fish can only live in an environment that has a proper pH level; also plants flourish best if the pH level of the soil is optimal. In a similar way, your body only operates at its best when its pH levels are optimal. Lifestyle factors such as smoking, alcohol consumption, eating too much animal protein, fast foods and refined sugars disturb the acid-alkaline balance of the body, thereby providing the basis for many diseases such as food intolerances, osteoporosis and candida (fungal overgrowth).

The suggestions below help to keep balanced pH levels.

Suggestions to keep pH levels balanced:

- Avoid or at least reduce the consumption of coffee, alcohol and sugar.
- Try to quit smoking. You might be interested to know that many of my clients, when undergoing Panchakarma, quit smoking naturally.
- Eat a variety of alkaline foods such as green leafy vegetables.
- Green tea helps in keeping a balanced pH level.
- Monitor your stress levels as stress can also increase acidity.
- Have plenty of fluid throughout the day, preferably good quality water, and avoid fizzy drinks.
- Drink your lemon/lime drink first thing in the morning as it alkalises your body.
- Have a green drink/smoothie in the mornings. (see below)

Green Drinks

If you choose to give your digestion a bit of a break and also to alkalise your system, have a green drink in the morning. Besides its excellent effect in reducing high acidity, here are some other reasons why introducing this drink on a daily basis will help improve your health and wellbeing:

- improves energy levels and brings mental clarity
- reduces cravings for sugars and refined carbohydrates
- supports weight loss
- proven to be helpful in counteracting the effects of radiation from travelling by plane and from Wi-Fi
- helps chelate toxic metals naturally.

Green Drink Recipe

Ingredients:

- 2–3 handfuls (approx. 100grams) of green leafy vegetables such as organic spinach, chard or kale
- 1 organic pear or apple
- 2–3 dates, de-stoned (optional)
- juice of ½ lemon or 1 lime
- 1–2 cups water
- ½–1 inch piece of fresh ginger root
- 1 handful of nuts and seeds such as chia seeds, hemp seeds, sunflower seeds, pumpkin seeds, brazil nuts, almonds
- some xylitol sweetener if needed

Directions:

Blend the greens in the water first, for about one minute. This ensures all cellulose is broken down and the fibre still remains in the drink, in contrast to juicing. Then simply add all the remaining ingredients and continue to blend until smooth. This makes approximately one litre of green drink, which can be kept in the fridge in a glass jar and drunk throughout the day. You may find that the drink slightly thickens after a while; in that case you can add some warm/hot water if desired.

Try to alternate your greens. You can also add some spices such as ¼teaspoon ground cardamom, ¼ teaspoon good quality salt such as rock or sea salt. Adding some fresh herbs such as coriander or fresh mint can be a nice twist to the drink.

If you want to make it a more sustaining drink, you can add half an avocado and some good quality protein powder; however, the best alkalising effect is produced if you use the recipe as mentioned above.

The best investment I have made in my kitchen of late is the 'Vitamix' blender. Not only is it useful in blending the drink in no time, but you can prepare a delicious hot soup in five minutes as well.

Spice Up Your Food

Benefits:

- reduces cravings
- makes food more digestible
- can neutralise any unwanted side effects of certain foods
- increases the body's bioavailability
- supports nutrient absorption
- prevents indigestion such as gas and bloating
- brings emotional satisfaction

Spicing is treated as an art in Ayurveda. It adds colour, aroma and taste to any dish. But there is much more to spices than we can see, smell and taste. The concept of spicing in Ayurveda is that is can be used to make food more digestible and to increase its bioavailability– the body's capability to absorb nutrients.

Appropriate use of spices can also neutralise the unwanted effects of certain foods. By this I mean what spices to use, when and in which order. A general guideline in Ayurveda is to fry spices as listed below. This is to ensure that each individual spice is fried long enough to unfold its flavour and to release its energetics.

As mentioned at the beginning of this chapter, it would be too much to go into great depth into the art of spicing in Ayurveda; however, the spices that any well-equipped kitchen should have are preferably:

- the seeds of cumin, coriander, fennel, fenugreek and ajwain
- ginger, turmeric, cinnamon, cardamom, hing (also called asafetida)
- black mustard seeds, rock salt or sea salt of good quality,
- dried curry leaves and dried herbs such as basil, parsley, tarragon, rosemary.

I encourage you to play with these spices. Be creative in the kitchen and don't be afraid. A subtle blending of some of the above-mentioned, or perhaps more exotic spices with Mediterranean herbs, can create an interesting tasting dish.

If you are not used to cooking with spices, just explore one or two at a time. Should you use seeds and spices in your food, here is the suggested sequence as to how to best use them:

- Warm up good quality oil or ghee (see how to prepare below) on medium heat. The appropriate temperature can be measured by dipping a wooden spoon into the heating oil or ghee. When bubbles start to accumulate around the wooden spoon, spices can be added. Smoke is a sign that the oil is burned and should no longer be used.
- First add asafetida to the ghee or oil.
- Next step add black mustard seeds and wait until they pop.
- Next add fresh or dried curry leaves and fry them for a few seconds.
- Following that, other seeds such as cumin, fennel, ajwain and fenugreek, can be added. Wait for a few seconds.
- Next in sequence are powdered spices followed by dried herbs. It is best to remove the pan from heat immediately after adding the powders to prevent them from burning.
- Any salt should be added in the middle or towards the end of cooking.
- Fresh herbs such as coriander, parsley and basil, as well as lemon or lime juice and fenugreek leaves, should be added just before serving.

Have a Liquid Day Every Month

Benefits:

  gives your digestion a break
  supports detoxification
  improves cellular metabolism
  increases energy
  supports weight loss
  brings mental clarity and emotional balance
  increases self-awareness

The best day to do a liquid day is around the time of a new moon, ideally on a Saturday. New moon supports detoxification and Saturdays, according to medical astrology, are known to be the best days to enhance the positive effects of fasting. I also recommend you make sure that on the day you plan to give your system a break that you have plenty of rest and reduce your activities. Writing down a list of emotions, behaviours or thought patterns that you wish to get rid of will also support the cleansing process. Practising the Agni Mantra as mentioned early in the chapter will also add to the effectiveness.

Again, as with anything in Ayurveda, there is no 'one size fits all' when it comes to fasting. It very much depends on your metabolic type and your bio-individuality; therefore, I suggest consulting with an Ayurvedic professional prior to starting a fasting regime for best results. Ayurveda recommends having short periods of fasting on a regular basis rather than lengthy fasting sessions, as this will increase your Vata. And also, from an Ayurvedic perspective, in the long run lengthy fasting will slow down your metabolism.

Regime on Liquid Day

- Have your lemon/lime drink with warm water and honey first thing in the morning.
- Do your Garshana skin brushing with silk gloves before your shower.
- Prepare your green drink as mentioned above. **Important:** for optimal benefit, especially when aiming at losing weight, I suggest you keep the recipe simple and don't add any nuts/seeds, avocado or protein powder.
- Prepare plenty of the green drink and have whenever you feel hungry.
- Throughout the day sip plain hot water every 15–30 minutes. This is essential to stimulate your cellular metabolism and to cleanse your tissues; have approximately 1 ½ litres by the end of the day.
- For lunch have some 'rice water', prepared as follows:

Rice Water

Take a handful of white basmati rice and wash and boil in 2 litres of water until very soft and starting to melt when squeezed between your fingers. You may have to add more hot water during the cooking, depending on the quality of the rice. Strain and spice the liquid to taste.

Pungent: Add fresh ginger to the boiling water from the beginning, and then add black pepper and turmeric in small amounts e.g. one heaped knife tip is sufficient. Also, add some cumin and the *Ayuwave* Metabolic Booster Spice Blend. The Metabolic Booster Spice Blend can be added alone or combined with the *Ayuwave* Agni Spice Blends, according to your metabolic type. Add a little salt for taste. Add some ghee, ¼–½ teaspoon, depending on the amount of liquid and on your digestive power.

Mild: Add less fresh ginger, coriander, cumin and very little turmeric. Use the *Ayuwave* Agni Spice Blend for an overactive metabolism, a pinch of rock salt or sea salt, some ghee and a pinch of black pepper.

- Using a greater or smaller quantity of spices can simply influence the pungency.
- During the day, keep drinking your hot water and one or two glasses of the green drink if you get hungry.
- Ensure you have plenty of rest during the day.
- Spending some time in fresh air by going for brief walks is fine; but heavy exercise is not encouraged.
- Make it a 'you day' by perhaps booking in for a relaxing massage. Have a warm bath (see suggestions in *Chapter Five*), practice yoga and meditation, journal your 'needs and wants', and create a vision board for yourself.
- Go to bed early.
- For dinner prepare your Rice Water again, as described above, ora clear vegetable/chicken broth, prepared as follows:

Vegetable/chicken broth

Put any leftover bones and skin from an organic chicken into a large stockpot and cover with cold water, approximately 3 litres. Add vegetables such as celery, carrots, parsley, coriander, broccoli, spinach, onions or leek if desired. Prepare your spice mix as suggested under the section *Spice Up Your Food* and add to the liquid. Add the

Ayuwave Metabolic Booster Spice Blend, additional salt and black pepper if needed.

Bring the liquid to the boil and simmer uncovered on low heat for approximately 3–4 hours. Check the liquid occasionally, skim off the foam and add more water if needed.

Strain the stock and ingest the liquid hot.

If you decide to prepare the stock for future use in soups, you can reduce the stock by simmering a few hours longer and make it more concentrated. Store stock in the fridge.

Consider Using 'Ghee' – Clarified Butter

Benefits:

- enhances the flavour of your dishes
- stimulates digestion if used in small amounts
- heat resistant
- can help in maintaining cholesterol balance
- rich in Vitamin A, D, E and K
- contains important antioxidants

For many decades, research led us to believe that diets high in cholesterol and saturated fats would cause coronary heart disease, which can lead to heart attacks. In fact, in the 1970s, the US government, the American Heart Association, the American Cancer Society and other groups started a massive campaign to convince people to stop eating foods containing a lot of fat. Fortunately, a few decades later, research experts had to admit that they were wrong.

The *Journal of the American College of Nutrition* published an article in 2001, where researchers at the Harvard School of Public Health, who previously advocated the 'lipid campaign', admitted that the 'low fat campaign' was based on little scientific evidence and that it may have caused unintended health consequences. Around the same time, evidence was found that the actual culprit for an increased risk in heart diseases and diabetes wasn't the fat but the easily digestible carbohydrates.

In 2008, a study funded by the Robert Atkins Foundation was published in the *New England Journal of Medicine*, where it was explained that people on a low carbohydrate diet, high in fat (including saturated fat), had the best cholesterol levels in comparison to those people who were eating a low fat and high carbohydrate diet. Interestingly, this is exactly the opposite of what was advocated earlier by the experts.

This perhaps should give you some peace of mind that using ghee or clarified butter, high in saturated fats, can be helpful in maintaining good cholesterol levels. As with anything it is very much about the quantity. Use ghee as you would use any other fat, for example, two to three tablespoons per day.

Many cooks often use ghee because of its high smoke point in comparison to other fats, in particular to butter. In general, heating vegetable oils high in polyunsaturated fats can be unhealthy since it produces various free radicals, which are reactive molecules that affect normal cellular health, thus leading to many diseases. Ghee has a very high smoke point and doesn't burn easily during cooking. Ghee has stable saturated molecular bonds and so is less likely to form the dangerous free radicals when cooking. The body also metabolises ghee's short chain of fatty acids very readily.

Ghee is known to be full of fat-soluble vitamins such as A (helps preserve good vision), D (prevents bone loss), E (good for the skin) and K (essential for blood health and protein modification). Ghee contains lots of dietary fats, mostly saturated fats that help your body to absorb and make use of these vitamins. In addition, ghee contains the antioxidant conjugated linoleic acid (CLA). CLA is being increasingly studied because of its cancer protective potential.

In summary, scientific evidence supports that ghee has health benefits if used in moderation; therefore, instead of avoiding ghee and saturated fats, it is healthier to avoid easily digestible carbohydrates such as refined wheat (pasta and bread), white rice, white sugar and white potatoes.

How to Prepare Ghee

1. Place one pound (450grams) of unsalted organic, or the best unsalted butter you can purchase, in a deep stainless steel or Pyrex-type glass pan on medium or medium low heat. This makes approximately 1½ cups or 350millilitres of clarified butter. I suggest you always start with at least 25% more unsalted butter than the amount of clarified butter needed, as the volume reduces during the melting and straining process. Remember, cheap butter contains lots of water and chemicals and burns easily.

2. In the next 30–40 minutes the water will boil away (approximately 20% of the butter is composed of water). Milk solids will appear on the surface of the liquid and also at the bottom of the pan. Watch to make sure that the butter doesn't scorch whilst melting.

3. After some time the liquid becomes clear and golden in colour. When you see the liquid bubbling and looking transparent, with white foaming on top and milk solids at the bottom, you can sprinkle just a little water with your hands on the foam. This will help to separate the foam and the milk solids will sink easily to the bottom.

4. Be ready to remove the liquid from the heat as milk solids on the bottom of the pan turn golden brown; otherwise, the ghee may burn. At this point, you may notice that the ghee smells like popcorn and tiny bubbles may rise from the bottom.

5. Strain sediment from ghee whilst hot, pouring it into a stainless steel or Pyrex-type pan. Strain by pouring through a cotton cloth placed over a stainless steel strainer. At this point it is very hot, so you should always be cautious.

6. Keep the ghee aside for five minutes before pouring it into clean glass jars, preferably earthen pot or Miron glass (see section earlier in this chapter). Ghee can be stored at room temperature and protected from sunlight. Make sure the container is always covered, as it draws impurities form the environment. Later whilst cooling down, ghee becomes solid; just heat it slightly and it will return to liquid.

Important Note:

Caution should always be observed when handling hot liquids. Ghee should never be left unattended during this heating process.

Variation:

If you wish to enhance the cholesterol balancing effect of ghee you can add ½ teaspoon of turmeric powder whilst melting one pound of butter. Turmeric is known to be a great cardiovascular protector and is rich in antioxidants.

Perhaps a week had passed since the phone call and still no improvement; Dad's situation was still critical.

I remember clearly that it was a rainy and cold Saturday afternoon – a day off work with no pruning of trees in the cold and no icy fingers – when it occurred to me all of a sudden that my dad could not leave the physical because I hadn't said good bye to him. He was waiting for me. I felt awful and all of a sudden a feverish cold washed over me – no warning signs, a runny nose and a sore throat. I sat down in front of the fireplace writing a long letter addressed to my dad. For hours I poured out my thoughts on pieces of paper as quickly as the rain washed down the window panes in the living room. After hours of writing, I burnt all the paper and whilst watching the words dissolve in the bursting flames, I felt more and more empty but somewhat relieved.

I went to bed in peace that night and around 4am I was woken up by a vivid dream. I saw my father on the front door of our family home in Germany with a big smile on his face, waving, as strong and healthy as I remembered him many years ago. A phone call from my brother two hours later confirmed my feeling that my dad had passed away peacefully at 4 am New Zealand time.

These 'father' events over a period of almost ten years plus the series of incidents that followed, especially after having visited the sacred land of Uluru in Australia, had given me the courage to trust my gut instincts more and more.

Feeling torn between the comfort of the known and the fear of the unknown, I decided the night my dad passed away to leave the organisation and to move to New Zealand permanently. I was wearing a shoe that had become too small and urgently needed changing. It was time for me to move on, to put into practice all the valuable knowledge and experience I gained over a decade. Having devoted ten years, at a very young age, to a spiritual organisation where my main goal had been to chase 'enlightenment', I slowly realised that I wasn't going to find fulfilment and satisfaction in that environment in which I had been for so long. It had given me the greatest gift in my life: expansion of awareness, exploration of my higher self. I had been given a glimpse of what resonates with me as the truth of life. But I knew I had to break away from all of that and pave my own path.

I left with nothing in my hands–no diploma, not even a valid certificate of completion, no endorsement. Just a heart enriched with a sense of trust and inner knowing; a soul that had become more mature, ready to explore the realities of life with all its difficulties and challenges. With the decision to take responsibility for all I had done so far in my life and the intention to do things differently, I kindled a huge fight with my ego when I was asked a couple of years later to further my training in Ayurveda and to do a formal qualification.

After a rough battle against my own narrow-mindedness and arrogance, which was trying to convince me that I had spent such a lot of time and money on my training already, I finally gave in. And this was when my life took a turn for the better.

I had to drop my ego, and after deciding to study Ayurveda in its great depth, not necessarily as an awareness approach to wellbeing but as a medical system of health care, the synchronicity of events allowed my Ayurvedic talent to unfold in its own unique way.

The choice to leave the organisation was very much a black-and-white decision; however, this book allows you to make more informed decisions. Just as I always had great help along the way, I see myself today as a sounding board to assist you in your decision- making process towards improving your health and wellbeing. Over the course of your personal journey, you will learn to recognise the inner voice that is always there. Learn to tune into the hotline of your higher self; the invisible hand that always reaches out to you and can guide you through life if you grab it.

The journey itself can be overwhelming. But my intention in this book, especially this chapter, is to present you with practical, action-based steps that you can take to empower you and that link in with the needs of your higher self. It is an invitation to do things differently; to invite synchronicities to flow in your life by accepting change so you never look back.

What If

- What if every aspect of your daily life moves towards the maintenance of your ideal weight?

- What if you freed your mind from the burdens of the past that will then allow you to step lightly into the future?

- What if you clear your personal slate of deeply held toxins leaving a fertile ground for optimal health and wellbeing?

Call to Action

Find a quiet space and reflect upon which body you think needs help or attention first.

Go through the list of suggestions in this chapter and make a note of the advice that works mainly on your chosen elemental body.

Initially, just choose one or two of the many suggestions mentioned in this chapter that appeal to you and which you think can be easily introduced into your daily life.

Keep a daily journal for a minimum of ten days and write down the effect those changes have on you and the various elemental bodies, keeping in mind that you may feel the change on a different elemental body, as indicated in this chapter.

Amrita – Nectar of the Natural Health Matrix:

- If you keep doing what you have always done, don't expect things to change.
- Introduce one thing at a time based on the understanding that less can be more.
- Practise awareness and trust your gut feelings.
- Be consistent with your practice.

FIVE ~ WATER

The Feel-Good Approach to Wellbeing

Another sleepless night; it was past midnight on a warm summer's night. My thoughts circled around in my head, creating this buzzing noise that drove me crazy. I desperately tried to use my mantra, do the breathing. But these repetitive thoughts only kept getting stronger the more I tried to resist them. They washed over me like a wave on a stormy day, making me gasp for air, unable to let go and accept I was about to drown. My heart ached, pounding as if I had lifted heavy weights at the gym; another panic attack forcing me to get out of bed.

"I have to go for a cliff top walk along the beach. I will be back soon..."

That night was like being on the fastest, most dangerous rollercoaster ride in Disneyland. I was walking as if I had drunk a whole bottle of whiskey, feeling sick, sick of life, sick of my situation. The presence of a shadow, which I had ignored all my life, kept tapping me on my shoulder more and more forcefully, making its presence clearly felt, pushing me closer and closer to the edge of the cliff. If only I had the courage to jump, I would. There are no words to describe how I felt that night trying to come to terms with my situation. After hours of walking, I finally broke down. The only comfort was the soft, velvety grass. Sobbing tears and screaming aloud, "Dad, Dad... why can't you help me? Why do I have to go through this? Why, why didn't I realise earlier?"

For months now my brain went through a continuous cycle, like tumble-drying clothes in a washing machine. I was searching for an answer, asking for help, praying for this phase to go away. I was so confused. My whole world was about to crumble as if someone had pulled the carpet beneath my feet. The shadow whisperer became stronger and stronger, forcing me to stop running away from myself and to embrace what could no longer be ignored.

I had always been brilliant in turning my back on what I didn't want to see. I was a master in pretending all was fine; but this time it had really hit me hard. No more running away. Wherever I looked, the shadow followed me and reminded me that there was no escape possible. I had to face my deepest fear, step into the lion's den and fight the battle.

Enough tears had been shed; there were three in this relationship, although we knew of each other's presence and tried our best to make it work. For sure it was a crowd.

In This Chapter We Discuss:

- The 'feel-good' approach to Ayurveda.
- How to dress based on your elemental body type.
- How to choose colours that enhance your mental and emotional wellbeing.
- Elemental artwork to balance your five bodies.
- Essential oil blends that enhance your wellbeing.
- How to use gemstones to access to the five elemental bodies.
- Musical instruments and their relation to the five elements.

Why is This Chapter Called 'Water'?

This last chapter takes into account the importance of 'feeling good' when it comes to creating health. Just as having a meal at a beautiful place with a loved one enhances the experience of eating, which in turn positively impacts one's health, a million things happen in our daily life that don't necessarily relate to health but have a definite impact on our wellbeing.

So far, the previous chapters have dealt with understanding the principles of Ayurveda, individual make-up, dietary choices, detox regimes and a mind-body self-care approach to experience health. A negative emotion in a healthy body eventually results in poor health, and similarly, a positive emotion in an unhealthy body slowly shifts the body towards improved health. Our body is very similar to the element water. It takes the form of the container in which it is stored. Therefore, the way we dress, the smells we smell, the jewellery we choose to wear, the artwork in our living rooms, the music we listen to and many such aspects of our everyday life all impact our wellbeing.

Our emotions are like the tides in the ocean that directly respond to the cycles of the moon. In fact, the moon symbolises our mind and water is the connection between the mood and the moon. Hence, this chapter is linked to the 'water element' as it forms the medium through which the energy of the moon is carried to impact our minds. In the following sections you will find several useful tips on how to feel good and thus encourage the experience of improved wellbeing.

A Feel-Good Approach to Ayurveda

Each time I allow myself a moment of silence amidst the often hectic life in London, perhaps by simply relaxing in the park, enjoying the sunshine and watching the world go by, it amazes me how perfect and beautiful nature is; how in the most flawless way the five elements are reflected in the magnificence of nature. It is these five elements that set the foundation for the entire physical world. Ayurveda recognises these elements of space, air, fire, water and earth as the building blocks that weave the tapestry of the entire material existence. They dance 'the dynamic dance of creation', where every object is unique because it contains a varying ratio of these five elements.

These elements are responsible for forming your physical shape, the state of your mind and the way you relate emotionally to the external world and yourself. Within each of us, on each of these three levels, one or several of the five elements are more predominant. Ayurveda then combines these five elements into the three vital bio-energies or Doshas, which from your own unique nature, the essence of who you are, as referred to in *Chapter Two*.

Over many years of practice, I have found the concept of the three Doshas to be extremely useful when assessing and addressing your physical wellbeing; for example, how your organs function, the state of your metabolism, the state of your bodily tissues and the degree of toxins accumulated. Based on the three Dosha theory, I then work out the appropriate treatment plan. However, because many, if not most, diseases have their origin in one of the four subtler bodies, in particular the mental and emotional body, I have seen the need to go into greater depth when trying to understand the underlying cause of a physically manifested imbalance by assessing its origin in the subtler bodies.

Especially in the 'Vata-deranged' times of today, where nonstop stimulation and speed set the pace of life, I have often referred back to the five elements and how they impact the emotional and mental body, rather than its condensed version, the three Doshas. This is what then gave birth to the *Ayuwave Ultimate You Makeover Experience*, which I see as a crucial part of the feel-good approach to Ayurveda.

The Ayuwave Ultimate You Makeover Experience

The *Ayuwave Ultimate You Makeover Experience* entails an image assessment that looks at how your wellbeing, in particular your mental and emotional wellbeing, can be enhanced by considering the following:

- the way you dress, in particular your choice of colours, fabric and the design of clothes you wear
- the scents you use
- the music you listen to
- the gemstones that would be suitable to you based on your Vedic Astrology horoscope.
- the artwork you look at.

This assessment takes into consideration your elemental body shape—if you are a 'SB' (space body) or 'FB' (fire body) type, for example— and the mental and emotional elements with which you predominantly communicate to the outside world. We also discuss which element could be enhanced to create a more balanced relationship with your exterior world, which will help to build an image that is closer to the 'Ultimate You'.

Why Bother About Looks?

Chronic illnesses can have a devastating impact on your psychological wellbeing, often leaving you helpless, with low self-esteem and a strong tendency towards self-dislike. It is in these situations where you perhaps face one of the greatest challenges: to shift your mind-set from focusing on the dis-ease to being and feeling well. 'Look Good, Feel Better', for example, is a non-medical, brand-neutral, public

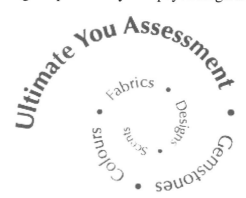

service programme that started in the USA in 1987 and is now operating in many other countries in the world, to teach women suffering from cancer how to look good despite their illness. This consequently has been found to influence their self-esteem in a positive manner.

The strong link between your emotional outlook and your physical wellbeing is no longer a secret. Expert researcher in Positive Psychology, Dr Martin Seligman from the University of Pennsylvania, confirms in many of his research projects how good feelings improve immunity and affect the speed with which healing can occur, be it from injuries or more serious illnesses such as HIV.

It is in those moments when I don't feel well, where perhaps fatigue and mental exhaustion wash over me like a wave, that on one side I want to pay even more attention to what I wear and how I look, but on the other side I fight between this inner devil that tells me, "Oh, I can't be bothered", and my self-awareness that pushes me to make an extra effort. Perhaps you can relate to this and, if so, have you noticed that when you manage to make the extra effort, despite really feeling down, people will walk towards you saying how great you look? This then becomes like an instant boost and shifts your spirits; you start feeling better immediately, your mood lifts and your mind clears.

From an early age I was very choosy when it came to what to wear. Even as a small child I loved getting dressed up, often to the dislike of my family, especially when being caught dancing in front of the mirror in my mum's skirts and shoes. No need to worry; the phase of getting into dresses is over. But I still can't walk past a shop window with a display of beautiful dresses or elegant shoes without stopping and admiring the designers' creations.

In this section of the book I want to share some of this passion with you, and perhaps inspire you to be more courageous, more playful, and to add more colour to your wardrobe. My grandma loved going shopping with me. She always made it a point to ask me to come along with her, perhaps because I have a natural eye for what looks harmonious and what doesn't. I don't shy away from wearing colours or styles that may be non-mainstream or unusual as this is a way for me to express my creativity and to play. For me, colours are a direct way to raise my body frequency and to lift my energy levels. This then has a knock-on effect on the way I feel and in turn how my mind functions.

If you feel the need for change but perhaps are stuck in the old, where lack of inspiration and creativity can make clothes shopping a daunting task, then as your personal *Ayuwave* Wellbeing Stylist, I will invite you on an exciting journey to discover the 'ultimate you'.

Dress Beyond Fashion

In my clinical practice I have some clients who find it very difficult to break through their fixed mind-sets and to shift some of their behavioural patterns. Even asking some people to go for a brief walk on a daily basis is a major issue, not because of lack of time but because of lack of drive and inspiration. It is often in these cases where I sense an openness to work form the 'outside in', which will allow them to surrender to change more readily.

A young woman of thirty-three came to see me in my clinic, mainly because of her eczema, poor memory and what she called 'mood swings'. Upon taking her pulse I realised the amount of heat and aggression that was stored inside. Her condition was very much influenced by her stressful life as a finance manager of a big company. Over a period of four months, we were able to improve her physical condition considerably; however, her mood was still mostly down and she lacked confidence despite her successful career in a highly positioned job. One day I asked her if she always wore black, even outside work. The answer was yes, and when I asked her why, she said it was because it made her feel safe. We agreed to do an *Ayuwave* image assessment where we discussed the relationship between her exterior appearance and her mental/emotional state.

Here is a shortened summary of my analysis and suggestions:

Analysis:

- **General:** lack of the elements of space and air, excess of the element of earth
- **Body type:** water – with rather small shoulders and wider hips
- **Emotional type**: earth– withdrawal and mood swings, tendency towards depression, lethargy, lack of motivation and flexibility, too serious and unapproachable.

  All of these were enhanced by the way she dressed: suits with trousers, short jackets that emphasised her hips, making her look short and bigger than she actually was, stiff fabric, colour black used in isolation indicated imbalanced space and earth elements.

- **Mental type:** 'fire' – internal heat, analytical and critical of herself, rigid in her thinking, serious and intense in nature. Wearing mostly black prevents lightness to come in on all levels, enhancing her rigidity and lack of openness and responsiveness.

Suggestions:

- **General:** increase the elements of space and air.
- **Body Type:** balance the 'WB' type by emphasising the need to wear tops that cover her hips, and to try skirts below-knee length to lengthen her figure. Also, introduce 'air' and 'space' fabrics that are more flowing and lighter, in particular when choosing her tops.
- **Emotional Type:** suggested introducing colours from the space and air scheme (blue and indigo tints) to allow her to get in touch with her higher self and to cool her down her emotional turmoil.
- **Mental Type:** adding the blues and indigo tinted colours of the air and space scheme will allow her to increase her creativity, her readiness to change and allows her to be more playful. This would also be supported by wearing dresses that are flowing and less stiff.

When she came back a couple of weeks later, it was hard for me to believe the person in front of me was the same young woman. She walked with confidence and mentioned that, by wearing the colour purple, she now felt that she was no longer alone and felt somehow more connected to herself. People started talking to her and complimented her on her makeover. Basically, what happened was she opened herself up to be seen and valued for what she does and who she really is.

The Elemental Colour Scheme

The sun is the brightest giver of light in this universe. Consider the actual colour of the sun as being white, and it is only when the light from the sun passes through the Earth's atmosphere that it changes to the yellow we perceive when we look up in the sky. The perception of colour through the eyes is a very complex process that wasn't understood fully until recently. The main centre for the perception of colour is in the visual cortex of the brain. Colour is not only perceived through the eyes but also via the skin by your sensory nerve endings.

The most complete colour is represented in its ultimate form by the white light of the sun; it is the pure Prana, or life-restoring energy of nature, which in its essence contains the full colour spectrum: violet, indigo, blue, green, yellow, orange and red. These can be seen as the seven rays of the sun, which very much influence your energetic body in different ways. I won't go into too much detail here, but what is important to mention is that from an Ayurvedic perspective, colour is like the Pranic life-force nutrition that energises each cell and keeps them alive.

Ayurvedic Concept of Colour Therapy

The concept of colour therapy or 'chromotherapy' goes back thousands of years to the Egyptians and to Charaka, one of the exponents of Ayurveda, who suggested the positive influence on sunlight in the treatment of particular diseases. In 1927, Ghadiali discovered the scientific principles that explain why and how different colour rays have various therapeutic effects on the body. His *Spectro-Chrome Encyclopaedia* is considered to be the first published book to explain the complete doctrine of chromotherapy, thereby demystifying the theory of chromotherapy.

In essence he discovered that each colour in the full colour spectrum has its own energy vibration, which can either increase or reduce the flow of energy through a specific organ. A varying intensity in the energy flow results in a different natural biochemical reaction. Each colour has a very specific effect on the different organs and organ systems of the body, and by knowing these one can apply the appropriate colour to balance the action of any organ or system that has become abnormal in its functioning or condition.

Colours are like gems that increase your energy field and raise your frequency. Any object on this planet, such as plants, animals or human beings, has its own characteristic frequency and, as mentioned in *Chapter One*, ill-health is nothing but an altered state of physiological functioning where external stressors such as environmental influences, medicines or food either raise or lower the vibration of living cells, organs and organ tissues. By introducing a corrective frequency, be it in the form of food, Ayurvedic therapies, herbs or for this matter, colours, help is given to the body to restore its homeostatic pattern.

Colour therapy predominantly influences your mental and emotional body by increasing your frequency, thus achieving greater balance on a physical level. Although I use colour therapy in my clinical practice through the prescription of gemstones based on your Vedic Astrology horoscope, which I will discuss in more depth later, I would also like to inspire you by suggesting that the same concept can be applied when choosing the colours you wear on a daily basis. Some colours can make you mentally and emotionally dull, heavy and inert. Others are more energising and some colours enhance the feeling of joy, harmony and serenity and bring you mental peace.

By knowing the colours you favour and those you dislike, you are telling a story about your personality and behaviour to the external world. For example, if you are someone who shies away from colours, you are most likely to have a loathing towards creative expression, such as music or dance, and you probably dislike children and the world as a whole. This nurtures feelings of discontentment, frustration and helplessness. The whole point of the *Ayuwave* Ultimate You experience, in particular the suggestion of an elemental colour scheme, is to bring you closer to your real self, the person you are in essence, by stripping away any mental and emotional behaviour patterns that could suppress your true nature and prevent you from being well and living a life to your fullest potential.

The following five colour schemes look at the fundamental, true colour of each of the five elements. You will see that this unique elemental colour underpins the entire colour range. For example, all colours of the air scheme have a blue hue to them, blue being the natural colour representing air.

Most of the five colour schemes have different hues and variations of the entire colour spectrum, the exception being the colours for the element of space and fire, and the reasons for that I have explained below.

Just remember that the three Doshas —Vata (space and air), Pitta (fire and water) and Kapha (water and earth)—are a condensed expression of the five elements. Their primary colours, that is, blue for the element of air, red representing fire and yellow the element of earth, inform the colour scheme for the remaining elements of space (indigo) and water (silver). The resulting colour range of the five elements below is by no means exhaustive. They are intended to be a guide only to help you when choosing colours that give you the 'ultimate you' experience.

Space and the Colour Indigo

The colour indigo to me is a fascinating colour because it best expresses the nature of

the awareness body. It is the colour of the *Natural Health Matrix*, since it instantaneously links your individual self with your higher self and thus activates your very own inner self-repair mechanism. Indigo in a way is also quite a tricky colour; on one side there is the colour black and on the other end of the colour spectrum we find the indefinite colour white. Indigo to me means 'all possibilities'– the potential to create anything you want. It can take any shape or form like the very nature of the element of space. It has to be used with care so as not to enhance some of its less conducive characteristic such as lack of earth connection and depression.

Effect on Mind

- expansive mind
- awareness of higher self
- deep spiritual understanding
- calms mind and nerves
- encourages deep meditation
- a mind full of vision and truth
- self-reflective

Effect on Emotions

- brings emotional balance
- uplifts your mood
- activates self-repair mechanism
- increased sensitivity
- brings a sense of contentment
- detachment
- sparks inspiration

Air and the Colour Blue

Blue is the first of the three primary colours and is the natural colour representing Vata Dosha in Ayurveda. This is why all colours of the air colour scheme have a hue of blue, irrespective of whether blended with the

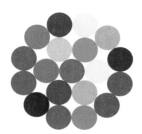

red or yellow of the remaining two primary colours. Depending on your true nature and the assessment of your mental and emotional state, I suggest you use the blue tones that tend towards the indigo of space, the reds of fire, the silvery hues of water or the yellows of the earth colour range. Blue is an extremely cold colour, especially the darker blues, and can be too much for a Vata personality; therefore, adding the warmth of fire and earth can be more suitable for those Doshic types

Effect on Mind

- brings peace and tranquillity
- encourages creative thinking
- stimulates clear thoughts
- logical sense of reasoning
- increases intelligence
- inspires mental control
- aids intuition

Effect on Emotions

- colour of hope
- cools down a heated temperament
- could lead to depression
- emotional indifference
- encourages self-expression
- serenity and trust
- symbolises loyalty

Fire and the Colour Red

You will probably notice that there is no hue of green in the fire colour spectrum below. This is simply because red, as the second of the three primary colours representing the natural colour of Pitta Dosha in  Ayurveda, when combined with different shades and tints of the blue of Vata and the yellow of Kapha, results in the colour scheme below. Red is an important colour in Ayurveda since it is responsible for digestion and all metabolic activities, especially on a cellular level. Therefore, even a person whose nature is naturally fire needs the red; however, adding blue in different shades and tints makes red 'digestible' even for a Pitta personality.

Effect on Mind

- reasoning ability
- independent thinking
- pioneering spirit, goal-oriented
- willpower, determined to succeed
- quick and sharp mind
- manipulative thinking
- ego-oriented thinking

Effect on Emotions

- colour of excitement and passion
- inspires courage and strength
- excites emotion and initiates action
- extroversion and confidence
- competitive spirit
- assertiveness
- emotionally demanding by nature

Water and the Colour Silver

You may argue that the natural colour of water is neutral, and this is correct. The colour of water is in fact neutral and able to take on different colours depending on what is reflected in it. For example, a blue sky when reflected in water makes the water appear blue. However, I have chosen 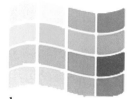 the colour silver or light grey as the underlying natural colour of water because it very much reflects a balanced emotional body, with a sense of serenity and detachment, able to relate and understand others with ease and comfort. The water colour scheme very much allows for all colours, but with an added tint forming the pastel colours of the basic colour wheel.

Effect on Mind

- controlled and steady mind
- mature thoughts of sophistication
- good mediating ability
- fair sense of judgment
- healthy critique
- radiates wisdom and good self-control
- strong values and morals

Effect on Emotions

- sense of calm and composure
- emotionally content and balanced
- impartial personality
- detachment
- least excitability
- sense of grounding and security
- formal and conservative expression

Earth and the Colour Yellow

Yellow, as the final of the three primary colours in Ayurveda, is related to the Kapha Dosha. When choosing the colour yellow as the colour of the element of earth, I definitely don't mean any bright yellow but  more the earthy yellow hues that go into the browns. These earthy yellow hues provide a sense of harmony, safety and security, like the all-embracing and all-encompassing nature of Mother Earth. Again, as before, the colour scheme below shows variations that are either linked to the red of fire, the silver of water or to the blue of air. The earth colour range does not have any hues that represent the element of space, since space and earth are opposites—one being the subtlest and the other the grossest of the five elements.

Effect on Mind

- mental stability
- can't be persuaded easily
- down to earth, practical thinking
- contemplative nature
- serious thinkers
- simple-minded and conservative
- a mind that encourages structure and orderliness

Effect on Emotions

- warm and supportive
- feeling of comfort and security
- honest and down to earth
- stable and reliable
- approachable and genuine with others
- closed and introverted
- needs security

The Five Elemental Body Shapes

The following table contains a description of the various elemental body structures and also gives you a visual idea how each element expresses itself in a different body frame. Your body frame is like a coat hanger and your body shape is what you put on this coat hanger. For example, if you choose to place a heavy coat on a tiny hanger, you may risk breaking the coat hanger. The key message here is to use a coat hanger suitable for the clothes you wish to hang up. In other words, your body shape should match the body frame. If you are disciplined enough and willing to make sacrifices in your life, you might be able to change your body shape; you might be successful in losing those love handles and undesired pockets of body fat in specific areas by sticking to a strict diet and exercise regime. However, you cannot change your body frame.

You are born with a unique body frame and stuck with that frame for the rest of your life, whether you like it or not. Thinking you can change that frame would be like aiming at transforming a banana tree into an apple tree. Perhaps if you are a magician, you will succeed.

What this section of the book encourages you to do is to:

- embrace your natural and unique body frame
- explore your body shape
- find creative ways to balance your body structure to suit your body frame by choosing specific fabrics and designs that balance the 'extremes' and will help to give you the 'ultimate you' look.

Call to action

They way to best use this aspect of the book is to find a quiet space and reflect on the effect of the elemental colours on your mental and emotional wellbeing as described in the tables below. Write down which of the qualities you think are missing in your life at this moment in time. Then choose one elemental colour scheme that seems appropriate for you, helping you to fill a gap or adding to the missing link.

You will find that you may not exhibit all the mental and emotional character traits as listed under a particular element. So be spontaneous and don't analyse too much; use your intuition. To give an example, you may feel emotionally frustrated and impatient, indicating an imbalance in the fire element; so you feel in need of mental stability, an emotional feeling of security and comfort. This means you could benefit from some Pranic earth nourishment.

Once you have identified the colour energy you need, you can go to your wardrobe and see what you have to fit the range of colours, and you can also meditate on the elemental artworks in this book. I discuss the aspect of using art to promote wellbeing a little later.

ELEMENTAL BODY SHAPE

SPACE BODY SHAPE 'SBS'		narrow shoulders and hips, extremely tall, thin face, high forehead, thin and narrow chest and abdomen, thin legs and arms, very little body fat
AIR BODY SHAPE 'ABS'		generally broader shoulders but narrow hips, legs tend to be taller, could also be a person of extremely short stature, usually non-curvy hips and smaller bottom, small face and neck, lower part of the body tends to be taller than upper part
FIRE BODY SHAPE 'FBS'		broad shoulders, muscular build, very even body shape, large head, strong forearms and thighs, very little body fat, generally well- proportioned face with strong cheek bones and neck
WATER BODY SHAPE 'WBS'		wide hips, slender shoulders and arms, generally shorter legs, relatively slim wrists and ankles, more body fat on lower regions of the body such as thighs and hips
EARTH BODY SHAPE 'EBS'		wide hips, wide shoulders, fat evenly distributed throughout body, more round in shape, soft flowing curves but also round and circular in shape

The Fabric and Designs of the Five Elements

Writing this paragraph is a challenge because in order to be able to successfully combine elemental colours, body shapes, fabrics and designs that enhance the 'ultimate you' experience, a one-to-one assessment is absolutely necessary. There are so many other factors that are important to consider such as your predominant, unique mental and emotional body type, the tone of your skin and your hair colour. It would simply stretch the 'frame' of this book to do that. Although there are some limits as to what you can do without a professional consult, but the information in this section of the book can be another tool of self-empowerment and can help you to work towards greater inner harmony and balance.

Let me share an example of how the choice of fabric, the design and colours, when used appropriately, can achieve mental and emotional balance and thus enhance your wellbeing experience, following the steps and principles below.

The Assessment Process

In the initial assessment your inherent elemental body frame and your current body shape will be discussed. Based on the evaluation of the state of balance of the four subtler bodies and your physical wellbeing, the missing element and how this can be enhanced will be defined, and one then looks at which element is dominating your current personality and perhaps needs harmonising.

The Assessment Principles

- Your body frame indicates your intrinsic 'ultimate you' personality.
- Your body shape dictates the designs and influences your choice in fabrics.
- If your body shape is in alignment with your body frame, you should choose the fabrics and colour scheme accordingly.
- Your body shape, if different from your body frame, sets the basis for your decision on the required action plan to re-align both.
- Your subtler body that is mostly out of alignment, be it the emotional or the mental body, should also be considered when choosing the colour scheme.
- On a day when you feel perfectly balanced on a mental and emotional level, choose the elemental qualities that you would like to enhance on

that particular day or for the particular occasion you get dressed up. For example, if you wish to experience more passion, excitement and strength, choose the fire colour range.

Example:

Body frame: fire

Body shape: air

Mental body: imbalanced earth energy, manifesting as rigid thinking and inability to think out of the square

Emotional body: imbalanced fire energy, expressed in suppressed anger and frustration

In this example, the body frame differs from the body shape. In the process of the *Ayuwave Ultimate You Makeover Experience,* ways will be discussed as to how to re-align both by aiming at transforming the air body shape to the naturally inherent fire body frame though lifestyle, nutritional and behavioural changes as discussed in Chapters One to Four. In addition, the imbalanced mental and emotional body will be harmonised through the feel-good approach to Ayurveda as considered in this chapter.

Fabric

Given the above example, the body shape can be described as the 'AB' (air body) type, with broader shoulders and smaller hips, the inverted triangular shape. Here I would be careful in using fabrics that relate to the air family such as crepe de chine and cotton voile because it would enhance the already 'airy' nature based on the principle of 'like increases like'. Perhaps the top could be made out of one of these fabrics; however, I would suggest using more grounding and stiff fabrics such as wool or raw silk for the bottom part. Whether I would suggest trousers or skirts would depend on the occasion, overall appearance and predominant behavioural manners of my client.

Design

Considering the 'inverted triangle shape' I would suggest wearing tops that nicely embrace the upper body; that fit well and are not too loose. The design should not enhance the already broad shoulders and upper body. Another important aspect to keep in mind when choosing designs for the tall 'AB' type is that their lower body is usually quite long in comparison to the upper body, which means the designs should even out the proportion. This can be achieved by wearing tops that slightly cover the waist line, for example. Also, perhaps fabrics with distinct patterns could help here to enliven the stagnant earth energy of the mental body.

Colour Scheme

The two elements that are clearly lacking and non-present are the elements

of space and water. Considering that the 'EF' (emotional fire) energy seems most out of balance, to a higher degree than the 'ME'(mental earth) energy, I would choose the colours of the water range as they bring a sense of composure and balance, and they calm and cool down the inner turmoil of the fire energy. At the same time I would suggest choosing the violet or indigo hues. This way the missing space energy also gets introduced. If for any reason this is not possible, you could also choose to wear a 'space top' made of a see-through fabric such as chiffon or wear a flowing, see-through chiffon scarf that represents the space energy.

By using the above example, you get an idea as to how the *Ayuwave Ultimate You Makeover Experience* is applied in practice, paying particular attention to the way you look. Imagine layering your outfit with the appropriate accessories such as a balancing water or space scent, suitable jewellery, a haircut and colouring based on your natural skin tone and body shape. All of that would make the experience a truly ultimate one.

The *Ayuwave* Ultimate You experience as discussed in this section of the book, creates equilibrium on all the four subtler bodies by focusing initially on the mental and emotional body. This in turn raises your frequency, which increases your energy levels and therefore expands your awareness to open the door to your true self. The four bodies sing in harmony with each other and your physical body has no other choice than tuning in to that healing harmony.

It may take some time to build your 'elemental wardrobe'. However, I invite you today to transform the sometimes daunting and tedious task of getting dressed into a creative dance, which will move you through your day with ease, joy and contentment.

I feel blessed that I have found a team of people who share my vision. Mark, the stylist and colouring expert, and Nico, the passionate Italian designer who fully understands my language and feels the same excitement to 'dress beyond fashion', where fashion no longer is seen for its commercial value but with an added unique wellbeing purpose. Mark and Nico are brilliant. You can give them the task of dressing a group of ten women that might have a body shape, skin and hair tone that is alike, and therefore are in need of similar designs or hair styles. But when they dive into the pool of creativity, none of those women will look the same. They are able to decode my language into a piece of poetry that brings out an unimaginable hidden dimension of each person.

Call to Action

Go to your wardrobe and aim at categorising your clothes in terms of the five elements. Experiment with the different elemental energies by changing your colours and fabrics on a daily basis. Perhaps start with the space energy and throughout the week move to the earth energy. Keep a journal of your experiences on a daily basis. Also, observe and take note as to how your environment such as your family, friends and colleagues might react differently on different days.

The next few sections will further explore how different modes of nature such as elemental scents, gemstones, music and artwork can further enhance your *Ayuwave Ultimate You Makeover Experience.*

Essential Oils and the Five Elements

Essential oils could be considered as the oldest and some of the most powerful healing agents throughout history. The Pharaohs of ancient Egypt secretly exchanged the sacred Blue Lotus Oil with the Maharajas of India for slaves, gold and other precious goods. In fact, at some point in history essential oils were considered more valuable than gold.

Each essential oil has multiple usages and health benefits, but in this section I would like you to use them as a powerful means to re-align your mental and emotional body with your higher self. They bridge the gap between the individual self and higher self by acting as a mediator that connects the spoken word with your heart. Specifically, the sacred elemental essential oils described below become the wake-up call that enables you to speak the language of the 'ultimate you'. They help you in expressing and communicating your innate highest truth to the exterior world in support of fulfilling your highest potential.

You will notice that I have only mentioned one essential oil under each of the five elements. That's because the oils listed are the most powerful essential oils that I have come across and used in my clinical practice to experience the unique qualities of the five elements. Through increased self-awareness you will be able to perceive the amazing story that each of the elemental essences whisper in your ear, and when you then shake hands with the true personality and character of each of the elemental oils, you will be astounded how their magic unfolds and leads you to the fulfilment of your highest purpose, the experience of the 'ultimate you'.

It might be that initially you feel uncomfortable with some of the aromas. If that is the case, usually this is the oil you need most at this particular moment in time; so perseverance is the key.

Space Element: Frankincense – Boswelliasacra

Frankincense has been used in religious rituals of ancient civilisations for thousands of years. It is said that the Roman Emperor Nero burned more frankincense than all of Arabia could produce in a year at his wife Poppeia's funeral. Frankincense continues to be used in many cultures today for religious ceremonies. There are many different types of Frankincense and some say *Boswelliasacrum* from the region of Oman, Yemen and southern Arabia is the best.

Frankincense is known to aid in meditation by reducing the mental chatter; it definitely is the essential oil of the *Natural Health Matrix*. It cuts the ties that stop you from living to your highest potential.

Air Element: Spikenard – Nardostachysjatamansi

Spikenard is also known as 'false Indian valerian' and is oil that has been valued since ancient times. It is considered very special and mystical and it has been mentioned in biblical texts that Mary Magdalene used spikenard to anoint Jesus's feet during the last supper.

Spikenard is excellent to release the fear of the unknown and gives you the often much- needed push to jump into your future. It urges you to leave the past behind by creating peace with those that might have hurt you. It breaks the chains that you might be fearful of letting go and helps you to learn from the lessons of the past so you don't need to repeat them in the future.

I asked the question at the beginning of the book, "Are you living life or is life living you?" If your answer was the latter then the air element is out of control and spikenard will help you to take charge again by calming your mind.

Fire Element: The Blue Lotus – Nymphaeacaerulea

The Blue Lotus was used specifically in ancient Egypt as the symbol for good health, strength and wellbeing. It probably could be described today as the Viagra of ancient times, evoking passion and sexual desire, a sense of ecstasy and euphoria.

Blue Lotus essential oil helps you to tap into your innermost core, the source of creativity and inspiration. It is the oil that creates a direct link to the emotional body, your deepest desires, which allows you to feel emotions and form deep relationships. Blue Lotus essential oil further promotes tolerance and encourages you to let go of undesirable emotional patterns. It can also be helpful in relieving addictions and unwanted behavioural patterns.

Water Element: Rose – Rose damascena

Rose is seen as the queen of essential oils, extremely difficult to extract because of its delicate nature.

It is the symbol of love in ancient art and literature. This is also the reason why I have chosen it as the essence best representing the water element. It allows for the experience of the finer aspects of love such as compassion, forgiveness and trust because of its ability to calm any rough waters in a fraction of a second; its scent strikes balance and allows you to open your heart to help others; it encourages rejuvenation and growth. Rose is the key that can open any door; any heart that might have been closed because of grief and despair.

Earth Element: Sandalwood – Santalumalbum

Sandalwood is known as one of the oldest aromatic materials, with a history of at least 4,000 years. Today, it is considered one of the finest woods for carving furniture and ornamental objects.

The beauty of this oil is that it helps you to stay grounded, without losing the connection to your higher self. It connects the extremes of the five elements–

the grossest earth element, with the subtlest element of space. Sandalwood will help you to align your circadian rhythms with the rhythms of nature. It assists you to re-programme your brain to open you up to fully understand your true life's purpose. Sandalwood is an excellent medium to connect to your own inner self-healing abilities by calling upon the frequency of Mother Nature.

Call to Action

I suggest you familiarise yourself with one oil at a time, starting from space through to the element of earth. Carry the bottle with you in your pocket and keep sniffing on the oil throughout the day. Apply a few drops on your pillow at night and use it when meditating. Also use it in in situations where you find emotional turmoil and perhaps experience mental agitation and restlessness. Journal your experience on a daily basis, in particular the effect the oils have on your mental and emotional body.

Gemstones and the Five Elements

I first realised the power gemstones can have when I found myself in a gemstone factory in Thailand many years ago, holding a 100+ carat yellow, oval-shaped diamond. This diamond sent electrifying tingles from the palm of my hand throughout my whole body, to the extent that it became such an overwhelming experience that I had to put the gemstone down.

At the time, I was looking for a 3.6 carat yellow sapphire that had been recommended to me by an astrologer. I was asked to wear and try out different stones over a period of a few days to see what effect they would have on my physical, mental and emotional wellbeing. Specifically, I was asked to observe my dreams. Finally, the appropriate stone had found me. Yes, the interesting part is that gemstones find you rather than you finding them. I am not trying to make everyone who reads this book believe in astrology, but I would like you to at least be open to the idea that not all stones are suitable for everyone. Astrology, in particular Vedic Astrology, can be used effectively to determine 'your' stone.

In this section I will discuss gemstones in relation to the five elements and in particular their influence on the mental and emotional body. I have chosen one predominant gemstone for each element and three related gemstones that can be used to best balance its associated elemental body. The information shared here is generic and my choice of stones is based on its colour and predominant element only. However, I am aware that there is much more to gemstones such as the place of origin, chemical composition and hardness, all of which play an important role when choosing an appropriate, therapeutic stone.

I suggest if you are serious in exploring the effect of gemstones on improving your health in general or in addressing any specific health issue, you either have a session by an experienced gemstone practitioner or perhaps have an astrological assessment. This way, a very personalised stone can be chosen with its appropriate strength and quality to bring out its best possible health enhancing benefits.

AMETHYST
The Gemstone of Space – The Awareness Body

Related gemstones: purple fluorite, azurite and lapis lazuli

Gemstones of violet or purple colour establish a direct link to the element of space. They are the Matrix that connects you to your higher self. Depending on the depth of the colour of the gemstone, which can range from deep purple to light violet, it brings in the qualities of the space element in varying degrees such as expansion, abundance and all possibilities.

The colour violet is a combination of the primary colours of blue and red. Red is the energy of concentration, dynamism and activity; whereas blue is cooling, quieting and expansive. When combined in the colour purple, they bring a direction to the directionless, In other words, when both are combined, concepts and ideas are being made more practical.

Amethyst is the most precious and valuable gemstone belonging to the quartz family that falls under this category. Leonardo Da Vinci wrote that amethyst was able to "dissipate negative thoughts and quicken the intelligence". Thus it is an excellent stone that encourages awareness and healing. It also protects from negative influences and energies and thus reflects it sacredness. It is a crystal that brings in the element of love and self-love and opens you up to higher intelligence. It is also known to help in overcoming addictions.

Effect on mind	**Effect on emotions**
• enhances meditation • quiets the mind • refines thinking • strengthens intuition • supports inner vision	• calms emotions • brings contentment and peace • encourages experience of love • promotes trust and inner knowing • encourages release of sorrow and grief

BLUE SAPPHIRE

The Gemstone of Air – The Mental Body

Related gemstones: blue calcite, celestite and blue tiger eye

Deep blue crystals stimulate intuition and subtle perception. They help you see the unseen. Gemstones of the colour blue enhance the qualities and energies of the air element such as flexibility, creativity, movement and change.

Blue often is described as the colour of distance; in a sense the further away an object is perceived in space, the bluer it appears. This allows seeing things from a broader perspective, permitting for new insights and ideas, going beyond the known and seen, which naturally leads to a greater truth.

With many of my clients, I find they project a different picture to the outside world than who they truly are. The way they behave and speak often does not seem to match their true nature. This is a predominant pattern seen if the air element is out of balance, where one might become like a flag in the wind, changing values and beliefs depending on the state of mind, emotions and whom one talks to. In this case, Blue Sapphire or even a Blue Tiger Eye are the gemstones that help you to communicate your true thoughts and feelings to your environment; to, help you to express who you truly are with confidence and ease. Blue gemstones also assist you in getting the strength to handle diverse and complex circumstances.

Effect on mind

- increases concentration
- enhances creativity
- brings self-discipline
- releases mental tension
- stimulates clear thoughts

Effect on emotions

- encourages trust and acceptance
- cools a heated temper
- creates emotional coherence
- supports self-expression
- lightens the mood

RUBY

The Gemstone of Fire – The Energy Body

Related gemstones: red spinel, garnet and fire opal

Should one have issues with regard to suppressed anger or the inability to experience passion, then definitely red gemstones can be helpful in fixing that. Just be careful though as red gemstones often provoke aggression and can be too overpowering. Interestingly, those who naturally have a strong affinity to the energy of the fire element often feel drawn to more of the same, which could make them dominant and aggressive; whereas those introverted and timid personalities shy away from the colour red.

Red exhibits the qualities of sharpness, warmth and glow; like the heat of fire initiating change and transformation. It symbolises the life-giving colour of blood, which can help you to make dreams come to life. Red is also the colour of speed and danger– a warning sign of possible friction and destruction.

There is no other stone that represents the energy of fire stronger than the gemstone ruby. It is the stone that very much symbolises the energy of the sun, characterising action and passion. The energy of a ruby increases the Pranic life force, which on a subtler level can be compared to the oxygen supply to the cells, initiating rejuvenation and change, bringing vitality and youthfulness.

Effect on mind

- fosters determination
- sharpens the mind and stimulates mental concentration

Effect on emotions

- gives courage and self-confidence
- brings a sense of power and control
- increases desire and passion
- helps to overcome lethargy and

- improves intelligence
- enhances concentration
- helps being analytical

exhaustion
- excellent to protect from negative energies

WHITE PEARL

The Gemstone of Water – The Emotional Body

Related gemstones: white chalcedony, enhydro quartz and white opal

Pearls are formed in shellfish, especially oysters and mussels, as a natural defence against irritants such as a piece of sand. As a defence mechanism, the mollusc secretes a fluid to coat the irritant. This fluid is produced to counteract irritation and layer-by-layer a lustrous pearl is being formed. Similarly, pearls are very nurturing and protecting, especially against stress. As a moon- and water-ruled gem, it is balancing to emotions and enhances truth and loyalty by bringing a centring and calming effect. Pearls help you to connect with the ultimate feminine energy.

The colour white, representing purity and the complete energy of light, enhances qualities of wholeness and completion. It reminds you of the importance of staying calm by allowing you to connect to the present. White brings emotional balance, which permits you to see the truth. Nothing can be hidden from white; so for some this might be a difficult colour since hidden feelings can be exposed.

If you are seeking to find or develop emotional balance, or if you are aiming at connecting to your higher self, wearing any of the above gemstones can be helpful. All of the white or see-through gemstones can be useful in calming emotions by opening the heart and mind to heightened awareness, and they will help you to bring these energies into the real world. This is in contrast to the gemstones of the space element, where it sometimes can be more challenging to bring these higher frequencies into the physical realm.

Effect on mind	Effect on emotions
• has a calming influence and keeps mind steady and focused • helps controlling mental anxiety	• enhances personal integrity • allows you to experience sincerity, loyalty and truth • has a centring and calming effect

- gives capacity to enjoy and appreciate life
- reduces excess heat in brain and heart
- enhances meditation practice

- counteracts irritation and fosters nurturing
- helps to get in touch with feminine energy

YELLOW TOURMALINE

The Gemstone of Earth – The Physical Body

Related gemstones: citrine, amber and yellow jasper

Currently, the earth is undergoing permanent changes due to environmental influences such as pollution and radioactivity. Generally, tourmaline is known for its earthy properties, which combine all elements. In particular a yellow tourmaline provides necessary protection and nourishment to your body with its healing rays by clearing and stimulating each of the energy centres. Yellow tourmaline will help you to establish a closer and more harmonious relationship with mother Earth, and this in turn will influence the way you relate to and express yourself with the people around you.

Yellow gemstones are gently warming and soothing, creating a sense of grounding. They can be helpful in achieving goals. If you tend to procrastinate, these gems will help to get things done. Gemstones of the yellow group help soothing friction and give a sense of self-confidence; they help you to maintain a positive outlook on life by bringing a sense of relaxation through balancing all the four subtler bodies. Yellow stones reflect the richness and abundance of Mother Earth; therefore, they are often used to increase wealth and prosperity. They will help you in getting our own personal power. They help you to get to the core of who you truly are and give you the power to express it.

Effect on mind

- aids concentration and communication
- conducive to higher thought and creativity
- enhances understanding
- increases self-confidence

Effect on emotions

- neutralises negative energies
- dispels fear and grief by increasing understanding
- enhances flexibility and emotional balance
- helps to find inspiration

- excellent channelling stone for communication with higher forces
- aligns all energetic pathways

It must be emphasised that gemstones ideally should be of therapeutic quality. This means they have to be prescriptive and of a certain strength or carat and purity, with no flaws, in order for them to influence positively your physical, mental, emotional, energetic and higher self.

Call to action

The gemstones in this section were chosen based on their colour and energetic frequencies, linked to the specific element bodies. Each gemstone, even a stone of the same group, tells its own story and has its own unique 'personality'. I encourage you to invite the gemstone that you naturally felt drawn to when reading this section of the book to come to you. Again, it's about trust and how much you wish to work with stones, and if you will allow the stone to find you. I suggest you place the stone into the palm of your left hand, which is linked to your intuitive nature, your higher self, and sit or meditate with the stone and allow the stone to speak to you. Observe, in particular, its effect on your mind and emotions and write your experience down.

Ayuwave Elemental Artwork

Walking through the National Portrait Gallery in London can be overwhelming for me at times. Somehow, too many impressions, the masses of people and air conditioning exhaust me easily, making me want to sleep after a short while. Therefore, I generally choose my visits to galleries carefully, and I usually don't stay for longer than one hour. What fascinates me though is that there are those paintings, sculptures or artworks that suddenly grab my attention. Some artists are like skilled magicians performing a well-rehearsed slight-of-hand-trick and I can't take my eyes off their work. It is these magic artists, capable of taking me on an internal journey on the spiral of creativity, evoking certain emotions, visions and feelings that inspired me to include this section on the Ayuwave Elemental Artwork in this book.

Art Matters

The question you may ask yourself is "Does looking at artwork truly stimulate different parts of the brain, evoke different emotions and perhaps influence certain physiological functions such as heart rate and circulation?"

The answer to this is yes, and this has long been acknowledged by philosophers and visual artists. The American neuropsychiatrist and Nobel Prize winner Eric Richar Kandel has given birth to a new branch of science called 'neuroaesthetics', which combines neurological research with aesthetics by investigating the emotional connection between beauty and appreciation of art and the electrical impulses of individual neurons. Although there is still a lot of research to be done in this field, a project organised by Professor Semir Zeki, chair in neuroaesthetics at University College, London, confirms the above view.

A group of volunteers, when shown a series of thirty paintings by some of the world's greatest artists, showed increased blood flow in a part of the brain related to pleasure by as much as ten percent– the equivalent to gazing at a loved one. This may not say much to you; however, for me this is enough evidence to back up my rather contemporary approach to healing, which also led me to engage an artist to produce the five pieces of artwork related to the five bodies as displayed at the beginning of each chapter of this book.

Justina May Groeber, German-born New Zealand artist, writes about her paintings of the elements as represented in this book:

> *"Ever since meeting Thomas in New Zealand I have noticed a peculiar similarity in how both Thomas and I relate to the elements of nature. Coming from the entirely different perspective of the visual arts, I resonate strongly with Thomas's concepts of the elements, focusing on their deeper meanings as forces within us that ultimately shape our physical and psychological realities.*

I was excited therefore when Thomas asked me to paint each of the elements: space, air, fire, water and earth. Whilst working on this project I found myself increasingly immersed, visualising the raw materials of life through the language of colour and the evocative qualities of texture and light. Starting from mere visual translation of Thomas's concepts, the images eventually developed their own logic, melting together the sensual and symbolic into my own abstract landscapes.

In as much as trying to capture some of their material qualities, I let myself be guided by my own emotional responses to the elements:

Space

Over and above the thought of cosmic space, I treasure space in its everyday meaning as 'having space around me'. In this sense space stands for possibility, potential and acceptance.

Air

In comparison with space, my relationship with air is much more physical. Air is breath and every breath I take in life. Despite its coldness, I strongly relate to the lightness and mobility of air. Air seems to express my moods. It is impulsive and unpredictable.

Fire

Fire represents intensity to me through its strange combination of beauty and danger. I associate fire with passion, willpower and transformation.

Water

I have ambiguous feelings towards water, as it is life giving yet vulnerable and above all emotional. Water represents emotions that swell up inside, sometimes gentle yet sometimes overpowering.

Earth

Earth as the raw material for life encompasses a bewildering, broad and sometimes disturbing spectrum of associations from fertility and growth to decay, dirt, excrement and finally mortality.

Cycles of life and death seem to be what earth could ultimately mean."

Call to Action

Spend a minimum of 15 to 20 minutes, contemplating the elemental artwork in this book in a quiet and meditative environment.

Again you can be spontaneous and choose any particular point in this book to which you naturally feel drawn, or you can be more specific depending on the need. For example, if you wish to stimulate your digestion or increase your metabolism, just observe the artwork of the fire element, or if you wish to increase mental alertness, connect to your higher self or balance your emotions, meditate on the air, space and water artwork respectively. Alternatively, you can do a five body elemental cleansing by spending a minimum five of minutes with each of the printed art images.

Important: Before you change to the next image or before you complete the activity, after having gazed at the work for some time, close your eyes for one or two minutes and allow yourself to view the work with your inner eye and to transcend the image, evoking its subtler effect.

Don't forget to journal your personal experience.

You can order A1 print sizes of the *Ayuwave Elemental Artwork* by contacting www.aywuave.com.

Music and the Five Elements

In *Chapter One* I touched upon the effect certain music can have on plant growth, which perhaps on a purely scientific level could be questioned. You might struggle with the concept that plants respond to music; however, it is undeniable that music has a profound effect on human beings. From the soothing tones of classical music, to the beat of African drums, music has the ability to change your mood.

There have been many things that could not be explained scientifically in the past, such as the phenomenon of the 'placebo effect', which today has been well documented to produce a positive effect, simply because the brain 'believes' that the placebo will work. The power of the brain to heal, which can be called 'psychosomatic', may not necessarily be understood from a scientific perspective; however, it has been accepted as being true. In this context, the field of incorporating music into medicine has grown over the past two decades, and music therapy has now been linked to decreasing anxiety and distress and improving mood, quality of life and immune functions.

Perhaps some of the concepts discussed in this section of the book might not be scientifically proven; but from my own experience, when using Vedic sounds I have seen the effect certain frequencies can have on health and wellbeing. I hope you will not dismiss these things too quickly just because there isn't yet enough scientific backing to prove them.

Let's now look at the question, "What actually is music?"

In simple terms, music is sound, and a sound is nothing more than a wave. These sound waves have a certain vibration, which need a medium to travel. Space is the medium that allows sound waves to travel. The space has to be constructed in a very specific way to best carry sound such as the Concert Hall of the Berliner Philharmonics or the Sydney Opera House.

Anything in and around us has a particular vibration that travels through space. In other terms, this vibration produces a very specific sound or frequency, which the human ear usually is unable to perceive unless you are 'tuned in'. Pianos lose their tuning and guitars fall out of key. For centuries, the only sure way to tell if such an instrument was in tune was to use a tuning fork, and the same for singers in a choir, who adjust their voices to the humming sound of a tuning fork. Similarly, when exposing any of the five elemental bodies to the instrument with which it naturally resonates, the sound frequency produced by the instrument allows the particular elemental body to resonate with (tune into) that frequency, thus supporting balance and wellbeing.

Below I have linked specific instruments that, when played by a skilled musician, I believe can directly balance and harmonise their respective elemental body. For example, when listening to the rhythmical beats of African drums, you gain direct access to your earth or physical body, producing a sense of harmony or balance. Also, another way of looking at this aspect of wellbeing would be to see that by learning to play any of the five instruments discussed below, the learning itself will be a strong healing for its related and respective bodies. Take the example of 'fire' and the violin as suggested. Violin is an instrument that requires lots of precision and focus by the musician to produce a harmonious and melodious piece of music. The precision and focus that is needed is a great outlet for a 'fire' personality to calm down and to reduce any excess of the fire element. It also brings out the quality of fire if it needs to be enhanced.

Space and the Harp

The harp has been used for centuries to produce soothing music, which brings peace, rest and healing to the mind, body and spirit. Its therapeutic use was first mentioned in the Old Testament when a 'skilled harper', namely David, was brought to King Saul who was in a restless and fearful state. After David played his harp for the king, Saul fell into a restful, healing sleep.

On listening to harp music produced by a fine instrument and skilled musician, one is drawn into a state of emotional, physical and spiritual wellbeing. The harp has an archetypal resonance as an instrument of communication between the physical and subtler realms. Therefore, I suggest listening to harp music to connect to your awareness body. Harp music links your individual self with your higher self. The harp can be seen as the Matrix that directly establishes a connection to the area of natural health by stimulating cellular rejuvenation and repair.

Air and the Flute

To date, the oldest flutes have been found in the Swabian Alb region of Germany and are said to have been from about 35,000 years ago. This makes the flute the oldest woodwind instrument, where sound is being produced by the passing of air across the mouthpiece. Flutes have evolved over those thousands of years. Originally they were made from bones, which interestingly in Ayurveda are very much linked to the element of air, making it a perfect instrument to access and balance the air or mental body.

Listening to the tunes produced by a flute is known for its calming and relaxing effect. When played and listened to at the end of a busy day, the Native American 'spirit flutes' especially have a calming and restoring effect on the mind. Also, its player very much benefits from it as it is a great lung exercise that helps to increase lung capacity. Irrespective of whether you play the flute or simply listen to its harmonising tunes, it helps you to connect instantly to the present moment by increasing the flow of Prana or life force. As you might remember from the previous sections of the book, Prana is necessary to maintain equilibrium in your physical body as well as your subtler bodies, in particular the mental body.

Fire and the Violin

I find the best instruments to connect to your fire or energetic body are the string instruments, in particular the violin. The word violin comes from the Medieval Latin word 'vitula', meaning string instrument. The four-stringed violin as we know it today originated from Italy in the early 1500s. But the history of bowed stringed instruments goes back to the ninth century and were the typical instruments of the Byzantines and the Islamic empires of that time.

Of all the instruments, when played skilfully the violin can be one of the most beautiful instruments to listen to. Equally, when played badly, the awful sounds like fingernails on a blackboard, makes one want to run away. I have linked the violin to the fire body because its harmonising tunes can give you the necessary focus and determination to make things happen. On the other hand, its sound can be the perfect recipe to cool down an extreme fiery personality.

Water and the Singing Bowls

Singing bowls are commonly referred to as 'Tibetan Singing Bowls' and originally were used as a signal by Tibetan monks to begin and end a session of silent meditation. When played with a wooden stick, the metal bowl emits a resonating sound that assists you in finding your emotional centre. These bowls come in various sizes and traditionally were constructed of seven metals: gold, silver, mercury, copper, iron, tin and lead, which correspond to the seven planets: Sun, Moon, Mercury, Venus, Mars, Jupiter and Saturn respectively.

In my practice I have found singing bowls extremely useful when needing to connect to and align my clients with their emotional body. The purity of their subtle sound raises your frequency instantly and thereby allows you to experience a sense of calmness and inner peace. Any emotional turmoil instantly comes to a standstill by the vibrations of singing bowls, leaving you with a sense of joy and inner peace, comparable to the calm and clear atmosphere after a heavy storm.

Earth and the Drums

Drums first appeared as far back as 6000 BC; however, the concept of drums is as old as mankind itself. Drums have been used since then for various occasions such as indicating the beginning and end of wars, for ritualistic purposes, in celebrations and for pure entertainment purposes only.

More and more research is being published to confirm the therapeutic benefit of drums and so-called drumming circles. For example, an article published in the fall/winter 2003 issue of the research magazine *Advances in Mind-Body Medicine,* Meadville, Pennsylvania, confirms the health benefits of drumming on improving 'burnout syndrome' and improving mood states. It is also suggested that drumming might be useful in controlling pain, as it produces endorphins and an opiate like substance that the body produces naturally, which can be compared to the body's own morphine-like pain killers. This to me clearly indicates the immediate health benefits of rhythmical drumming on your physical wellbeing.

I have also found drums extremely useful with clients who are not connected to their physical body, such as when being poorly grounded, as it enhances their ability to function more effectively on a day-to-day basis. It maintains the necessary 'earthy' connection for those who naturally tend to be more in their mental or awareness body. It helps moving the mind out of conceptual thinking beyond time and space without losing the grounding effect. Drums can be seen as a tool for change where the stagnant earth energy has taken over and change is needed. Beating rhythmical drums also helps to naturally align your circadian rhythms with the cycles and rhythms of nature.

Although I strongly emphasise the need for creative expression irrespective of your elemental personality type, you may not take to the idea of learning to play an instrument that well. In that case, listening to the elemental instruments will be helpful. I suggest you find yourself a quiet and relaxed space where you can sit down undisturbed for at least ten minutes daily and listen to the music. It could be that initially you may find it difficult to relate to your natural instrument. In that case, I suggest you gradually start off with one to two minutes and build up to ten minutes over a period of a couple of weeks.

How selfish of me to think I could keep going and that it was all right for me to continue hurting the three souls entangled in this drama. Out of all of the challenges I had faced in my life, this by far had been the most difficult one; a situation I thought I would never be able to overcome or forgive myself for, a phase of depression with nowhere to go. I thought I could only end it by ending my life. After a period of six months, I had no other choice but to leave eighteen years of a harmonious relationship behind, a woman who had been a strong pillar in my life, who set me up on my path of self-discovery, who guided me on my own personal health journey.

With huge guilt and emotional scars to heal for all involved in this drama, I accepted the challenge I had chosen and reluctantly embraced my new life with a man who patiently waited in the side wings until I was finally courageous enough to cut the strings of my past.

Sometimes life circumstances push you towards a cliff, where you have no other choice than to jump. The fear of jumping, however, transforms into an indescribable feeling of freedom when you actually take that leap of faith into the unknown.

Towards the end of this chapter I invite you again to pause for a moment and take count of where you are at this particular moment in your life. Think about what actually drives your life: is it *you* or *life* itself? If it is life that has taken over your living then this is very much an indication that something needs changing.

> "The only thing constant in life is change."
>
> François de la Rochefoucauld

Don't resist change. This would be like resisting the nature of life itself, as so beautifully expressed in the saying above. Everything in and around you changes constantly: your thoughts pop in and out of your conscious mind, almost at the speed of light. One second you may feel elated and the next moment down and sad. Believe it or not, your lungs are six weeks old and your taste buds change every ten days to two weeks.

Renewal is the natural flow of life and what makes life richer. It is only when we resist that flow that we start to experience struggle and pain, be it on a physical, emotional, energetic or mental level. This is what eventually will lead to ill health.

Take the analogy of a dry branch on the tree of life. It needs nurturing from within by paying attention to its roots. The 'how to' has been covered in all the previous sections through the principles and suggestions discussed. However, I see this final section of the book as the external layering of oil applied with love and care to the dry, wooden branch, which will give it much-needed nurturing and flexibility that eventually prevents the branch from breaking, even in the greatest of storms– allowing you to live your life to its fullest.

The concept of 'dressing beyond fashion', the invitation to play with colours, gemstones, music, scents and the understanding of elemental artwork is a platform for inner change accessed through the external Matrix. This chapter challenges you to look at your environment and invites you to assess how much of that external environment reflects you and your true character. It helps you to get an elemental sense of what defines you and how you present yourself to your external world.

In the end, the choice is with you. You can remain a victim of life's circumstances or use the knowledge and newly-gained skills to operate the switchboard of your life. Why not embrace an approach that may push you beyond your comfort zone but in return will bring you closer towards an experience of the 'ultimate you'– greater happiness, contentment and truthful living, without which health and wellbeing is impossible.

What if

- What if You were given the tools to enhance YOUR inner and outer beauty allowing access to the ULTIMATE YOU experience?

- What if wellbeing flows through your veins continuously enhancing natural health and personal growth?

- What if all of your five bodies are aligned in such a way that your daily life becomes a blissful journey through your senses?

Call to Action

We have established throughout the book that having a balanced life is crucial to wellbeing. As part of this balanced lifestyle, expression of your creativity is important; therefore, I would encourage you to perhaps take up learning one of the instruments above. The choice of instrument very much depends on which of the five bodies you naturally identify yourself with.

As an example, if you are a 'worrier', this indicates that you are more in your mental body, linked to the element of air. Therefore, learning how to play the flute is a good way of expressing your creativity. If you have the tendency to 'feel' the world in and around you, perhaps learning and using singing bowls will be helpful since they are linked to the element of water and directly connect you to your emotional body. Similarly as a 'doer', earth element, who enjoys using hands and practical skills, you may consider learning how to play the drums or perhaps join a drumming circle.

For someone with a great 'trust' in the natural flow of life, where you are more naturally connected to the higher self or your awareness body –space element, learning how to play the harp might be quite natural. Finally, if you find yourself as a more 'analytical' person, who enjoys a debate, then learning how to play the harp will be the perfect challenge for you to express creatively your need for precision and perfection in life.

Amrita – Nectar of the Natural Health Matrix:

- Be open to explore gentle approaches to wellbeing that might lay outside of your current understanding.

- Don't be shy to add colour to your life.

- Dress beyond 'billboard fashion' to embrace your beautiful personality.

- Connect to the richness of Mother Nature through using gems.

- Use art as a form of engaging your senses in creating wellbeing.

- The Matrix of natural health is not complete without experiencing music that reflects your true vibration.

AYURVEDIC MIND-BODY QUESTIONAIRE

Tick as many responses as applicable in the following chart:

	Vata		Pitta		Kapha	
Body Frame	Thin, bony, tall or short		Medium, balanced		Large, broad	
Weight	Low		Moderate		Heavy	
Skin	Dry, rough, cool, dull		Soft, oily, warm, ruddy		Thick, moist, cool, pale	
Hair	Dark, dry, curly		Soft, oily, fair/red		Thick, oily, wavy	
Teeth	Protruding, big, uneven		Moderate, yellowish		Strong, even, white	
Nails	Rough, dry, brittle, bitten		Soft, pink, strong		Soft, large, white	
Eyes	Small, dry, dull, nervous		Sharp, penetrating		Big, thick lashes	
Appetite	Variable, small		Good, regular		Slow, steady	
Thirst	Variable		Excessive		Minimal	
Elimination	Dry, hard, constipated		Soft, oily, loose		Thick, heavy, slow	
Urine	Frequent but sparse		Yellow, copious		Infrequent, average	
Sweat	Minimal		Profuse, pungent in odour		Slow to begin, heavy	
Pulse	Weak, erratic		Stable, strong		Slow, smooth	
Blood Circulation	Variable, poor, sluggish		Good		Moderate	
Sleep	Light, disturbed, minimal		Sound, moderate		Heavy, excessive	

Speech	Rapid, high or hoarse		Sharp, cutting, loud		Slow, harmonious
Libido	Varies, directed in fantasy		Passionate, excessive		Slow but strong, loyal
Immunity	Variable, poor		Moderate		High
Activity	High, restless, mobile		Moderate, direct		Minimal, slow
Endurance	Minimal		Moderate		Excellent
Mind	Restless, curious		Aggressive, clever		Calm, slow
Memory	Short term		Sharp, good		Long term
Routine	Dislike		Enjoys planning		Adaptable, tolerates
Faith	Erratic, changeable		Fanatical		Steady, devoted
Moods	Variable, fluctuate		Express forcibly		Changes slowly
Hobbies	Travel, art, philosophy		Sports, politics, luxuries		Serene, leisurely types
Food	Simple, sparse, snacking		Require regular meals		Gourmet, luxury, fatty
Creativity	Original		Technical, scientific		Entrepreneurial
Sensitivity	Cold, wind, dryness		Heat, sun, fires		Cold, damp, humidity
Temperament	Nervous, insecure, shy		Determined motivated		Conservative, resilient
Dreams	Frequent, fearful		Erotic, violent, vivid		Romantic, calm

A FINAL NOTE

Wellbeing is a natural state of being and therefore is in reach of every single person on this planet. It is not exclusive to those that are gifted, nor can it be bought. It can be accessed simply through your own inner awareness. Ill health, dis-ease and an unhappy way of living is a sign that you have lost your connection to that most natural state of being. *The Natural Health Matrix* is a guide that helps you to reconnect to that area within you where ideal health and wellbeing is a given.

Just as the process of dying a white cloth requires the repeated dipping of the fabric into the colour of your choice, regular access to this most natural state of being eventually results in improved wellbeing. You may feel well even if you suffer from a specific ailment. The more you nurture this feeling of wellbeing, the more permanent this state will remain with you, adding quality to your living, irrespective of whether you are perfectly healthy or suffer from a specific ailment at this moment in your life.

Life tends to be emphasised by its beginning and end points, but it is more important to appreciate the experience of it– the journey. Someone could have lived eighty-five years but had a rather stale and miserable life compared to a person who died at the age of fifty, after having lived a happy life to its fullest, with many lifetimes packed into one. What is more vital?

In sharing some important milestones of my life in the stories at the beginning of each chapter, I hope to have triggered in you the passion to explore life and encouraged you to take risks so you can stir the boat of your life again, in a direction you want it to go. Be open to change, as with change there are new opportunities waiting around the corner, and sometimes these can be greater than you can ever imagine. When your elemental bodies work in harmony with each other in creating that continuous flow of energy, renewal becomes a permanent reality. One feeds off and nourishes the other, generating a state of natural ease and balance. It is at the intersection between your physical and subtler bodies where you can effortlessly access your *Natural Health Matrix*, which will lead you to the ultimate experience in life, which is nothing more and nothing less than… LOVE.

After more than two decades of exploring meaningful approaches to health and wellbeing in everyday life, I now feel more than comfortable with the direction I have taken. I apply what I have experienced and have come to discover my own approach to a clinical practice which is safe and effective in clients who seek my help through Ayurveda. Ayurveda is the science of life and therefore, just as with one's life, Ayurvedais like a river that changes its course in order to maintain the flow and not stagnate. As such, with technological advancements Ayurvedic Science has come to embrace the more holistic Quantum healing or Quantum medicine. Integrating timeless common sense approaches to health, as in Ayurveda, and cutting-edge scientific discoveries, as in Quantum medicine, is not only exciting but also highly relevant. Who knows what is going to happen tomorrow, or where our journeys will take us the day after. Celebrating each day of our lives and thanking ourselves for making the decision to embark on a personal journey to wellbeing is all that we can look forward to.

Thomas

ACKNOWLEDGMENTS

I would like to express my gratitude to a number of people who made this book possible.

Firstly, those who contributed when the book was still in its conceptual stage:

Shamim and Ivana, thank you both for your push and encouragement to start the process of writing this book. Without you, writing a book would probably still be something that I would do at some stage in the future…when I had the time.

Will, for guiding me throughout my journey as an author and for helping me to find my own voice. You have been such an inspiring coach and believer in *The Natural Health Matrix* from day one.

To all my clients and students over the past twenty-five years who have contributed immensely to this journey. Without you, this book would not exist. Each one of you, irrespective of which corner of the world you currently reside, opened my mind and nourished my heart by expressing your trust in the process and by allowing me to be myself.

To my spiritual guide Maharishi Mahesh Yogi, who initiated me into the vastness of Vedic Science and who taught me patience and faith in life.

Those who made the book come to life:

Sandra, for your ability to translate some challenging concepts into clear illustrations. Justina, a heartfelt thank you for adding colour to the book through your inspiring and amazing artwork.

Nico and Mark, for embracing the idea of 'dress beyond fashion'. It has been such a joy to work with you and to explore creative ways of making fashion and styling more meaningful.

Jorge and Sheila, thanks for sharing your vast knowledge and passion for gemstones with me.

To the editing team; Sue and Jonathan for erasing my 'Germanisms' and for keeping me in the right tense. Philip who went out of his way to expand on my rather limited vocabulary and with Lisa gave this book the final look.

Vicky for liaising with the printers and for rushing around to ensure we had printed copies for the book launch.

Charmian, thank you so much for your dedicated effort to spread the message of this book and for ensuring as many people as possible benefit from it.

My background support team who kept me going:

Susie, for believing in me and for always having an ear to listen and a hand to help. Christel, for setting me up on the path of self-discovery many years ago and for remaining such a loyal friend during my entire journey despite all the challenges and difficulties. My entire family for backing me up and pushing me to stay on track.

And last but not least, to my dear partner Vijay, who has been such an inspiring friend, colleague and teacher. It is you who has taught me true Ayurveda and pushed me to think critically and outside the square; who has helped me to find my own voice in Ayurveda through your selfless sharing and your treasured gift to integrate modern science with ancient wisdom.

Thomas Mueller

B.A, D.A.Med

Ayuwave Natural Health Clinic
57, Wimpole Street
London, W1G 8YW
United Kingdom
www.ayuwave.com
info@ayuwave.com

BIBLIOGRAPHY

Battaglia S (2009), *The complete guide to aromatherapy*, The International Center of Holistic Aromatherapy, Brisbane.

Fife B (2008), *Oil pulling therapy*, Piccadilly Books, Colorado Springs.

Gala D (2008), *Health at your fingertips*, Navneet Publications, Mumbai.

Lilly S & Lilly S (2010), *Crystal, colour and chakra healing*, Hermes House, London.

Melody (2011), *Love is in the earth*, Earth-Love Publishing House, Colorado.

Miller L, & Miller B (1995), *Ayurveda and Aromatherapy*, Lotus Press, Twin Lakes, Wisconsin.

Mueller T (2014), Increased awareness when there is a struggle to meditate, *Ayurveda Journal of Health*, 12(4), 35-37.

Muktibodhananda, S (2009), *Swara Yoga*, Thomson Press, New Delhi

Murthy, VS.(2012), Guidelines for practitioners in treating disorders of 'impaired Agni'. Integrating Ayurvedic model and evidence base in managing constipation predominant Irritable Bowel Syndrome, *Light on Ayurveda Journal of Health*, 10(4), 47-54.

Murthy, VS.(2012), Sanskrit and Science - the necessary links for propagation of Ayurveda in the west, *Light on Ayurveda Journal of Health*, 10th Anniversary Special Issue, 2002- 2012, 54-57

Murthy, VS. (2011), Ayurveda at the Crossroad of Evidence Base, *Light on Ayurveda Journal of Health*, 10(2), 70-72.

Schwartz, J & Gladding, R (2011), *You are not your brain*, Penguin Group, New York.

Van der Werff, T (2005), *Why are you wearing those colours*, Peaceful Living Publications, Auckland.

Wright A (1999), *The beginner's guide to colour psychology*, Kyle Cathie, London.